SPACE INVADERS

annual
1983

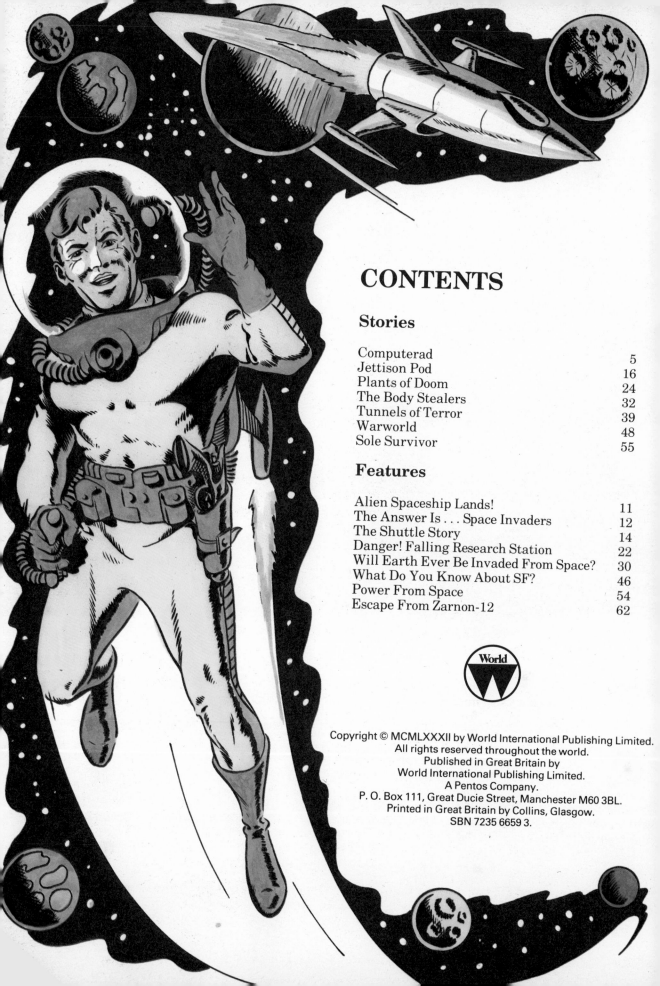

CONTENTS

Stories

Features

COMPUTERAD

The attack began at dawn when red and orange hued laser beams lanced down from the skies and blended almost artistically with the rays of the early morning sun. Those who could have observed from a neutral standpoint may have described the scene as picturesque, but the people of the planet Earth held no such feelings: they were too busy fighting for their lives.

Alpha 19 was the first of the Earth Defence stations to be hit, probably because it contained the most sophisticated battle computer of them all. As the explosions from impacting laser barrages sounded all around, crews raced to their war stations, desperately activating the machines that would launch weapons in a system of automatic retaliation. But it was already too late — the attack had been too swift, too deadly and too unexpected. The people of old Earth had a name for what had happened; they called it a pre-emptive strike. Refusing to admit that all they could do was postpone the inevitable, the survivors of the first blitz fought on, the death cries of friends and colleagues ringing in their ears.

One hour after dawn, Earth Defence Station Alpha 19 lay silent, the charred remains of men and machines disturbed only by the spattering drops of a rain shower that nature had despatched to cool the laser-heated surface of the planet. Those who had by some miracle survived fought back tears of bitterness as they remembered that men had had the audacity to think of themselves as the superior race in the galaxy. On that morning, in the year 2206, an attack that had lasted for a little over sixty minutes and devastated the face of the Earth had proven that they definitely, most definitely, were not.

"No, Commander!"

Commander Derek Thane turned back to the soldier with whom he had terminated conversation a moment before, aware that all other eyes on the prison shuttle had turned on him too.

"Look at you!" the soldier went on, "look at you all! These things have destroyed our world, and you just sit there like sheep! Sheep being led to the slaughter!"

Thane remained silent, knowing that if he spoke further it would only aggravate the soldier's frustration and anger. Thane had no intention of allowing himself to sit back and submit to the aliens, nor, he had no doubt, did any of the others. But now was not the time or the place; they had to wait, they had to bide their time if revenge for the almost total destruction of their race was to be successful. As the soldier continued ranting, Thane turned away and looked around at the other captives, his comrades in their own private little hell. Across from him, a girl smiled back, despite the fact that she bled severely from a wound in her leg. She reminded Thane of his wife, and all of a sudden his mind was filled with painful memories. Not so long ago, Thane had watched his wife die.

"What's your name?" he asked, trying to draw his mind away.

"Miranda," the young girl said. "I was a computations analyst at Alpha 32."

Thane introduced himself in name only, afraid that anything more would start the memories cascading again, although he knew that the girl already had heard that he was a Commander. "Alpha 32? That's the defence station at M'Garbi,

isn't it?"

"Was, Commander. Was," interrupted the soldier.

The snide behind-the-back remark made Thane's blood boil, and he spun around to grasp the soldier by the throat, realising at the same time that the events of the past hours had pushed him further towards the edge than he had thought; he did not normally behave so violently. Taking a deep breath, Thane released his grip. The soldier gulped.

Turning back to face the rest of the captives, Thane sighed. He knew now how difficult it would be to remain calm until the right time. "I don't," he hissed back at the soldier, "want to hear another wo . . ."

Thane trailed off in mid sentence, his mind staggered and humbled by the view that met his eyes. Now that he was standing, Thane could see out through the prison shuttle's viewport, and for the first time he saw what had attacked the Earth. Transfixed, Thane hardly noticed as Miranda stood up beside him and also looked out. "Oh my God . . ." she said.

Suddenly, shockingly, space was no longer infinite. The things that hung in orbit above the Earth filled the empty blackness as peas would fill a pod, their masses continuing out, out into space, until they seemed to be space itself. It was the alien battle fleet, and it was awesome.

The prison shuttle carrying Thane and the others sped into

the heart of the fleet, swerving and twisting as it avoided cyclopean protuberances and fearful weapons that still glowed with unimaginable power, seemingly a part of the ships themselves. Eventually, Thane felt the ship drag as retro-rockets and attitude jets came into operation, decelerating and positioning the shuttle for docking.

As Thane and Miranda watched, an immense docking hatch irised open before them and revealed a cavernous deck that would have held a thousand of Earth's largest battleships, but was only the smallest part of one of the alien craft. Slowly the shuttle began to move into the grip of tractor beams and was swallowed up.

Thane, Miranda and the others tensed themselves. They had arrived at their destination.

The subterranean level corridors of Earth Defence Station Alpha 19 were deserted and still, so when the chunk of debris toppled from a pile of smashed machinery and clattered to the floor, the sound of its echo lasted for minutes, although there was no one around to hear. Eventually, another chunk fell, followed by another and another. A hand appeared from underneath the wreckage.

It took the young boy a good few minutes of concentrated effort to remove every chunk of debris that was balanced above his body, but finally he pulled himself clear and stood up, sur-

veying his surroundings. The control room was dark and ruined, the floor covered in wreckage and the once alive banks of flashing, chattering computers now little more than scrap metal, but the boy recognised where he was and felt safe. It did not occur to him that beneath the wreckage lay the bodies of people he had once played with, nor that he had only by the most miraculous of miracles escaped the same fate himself; his only concern was for the scratch on his leg and how he could get it fixed.

Deciding on what he had to do, the young boy picked his way across the room to the door, trying to remember his way through the tunnels. The station was very quiet, he thought.

Where were all his friends? Mother and Father would tell him, he was sure. They would tell him what had happened. All he had to do was find them.

"All earth defence stations have been destroyed. All those who manned them terminated."

"Planetary communications?"

"Minimal. Civilian distress calls. Disaster reports. All defence transmissions have ceased."

"Good . . . good. The planet is ours. Prepare for second phase."

Derek Thane watched and listened as the aliens spoke, their gloating manner threatening to tip his trained composure into madness with every

second. Miranda and the other prisoners had been separated from him after docking, and he alone had been brought to the bridge, although for what reason he did not yet know. In front of him and below him, the sphere of the Earth hung in space, its normal green and blue colours hideously transformed into an ashen grey, pocked only rarely with isolated strips of surviving land. Until that moment, Thane had not realised how severe the attack had been, how much damage had been caused, and he gritted his teeth. He *would* have his revenge . . . somehow.

"Commander Thane. I am

Vant, Fleet Supremo."

Thane looked the alien who had approached him straight in the eye, wanting to defy him and fight, but recognising the need to learn as much as possible about the alien's plans. Thane stood rigid and said: "What do you want from me? What have you done with the others?"

The alien approximated a smile. "The others are of no concern. They will soon be dead. But you . . . you are of the utmost importance in the success of our phase two: the occupation of your little world for its resources."

"As Commander of Alpha 19."

"Precisely," the alien nodded. "You are the sole surviving officer of Commander rank that we have been able to find – we want your knowledge of your planet's remaining military capabilities. We know that you have that knowledge."

So that was it, Thane thought. The aliens were not satisfied with wiping out nine tenths of the planet. They wanted details of surviving bases, groups of survivors capable of retaliation, remaining weapons. They wanted to complete the job before they descended to the surface. They did not want to endanger one of their hides.

Thane smiled; whether any weapons survived or not, and he wasn't sure, he had no intention of co-operating. "Not a chance," he said.

"Not even to save your own life?"

Thane snarled. He had seen his wife and friends obliterated, seen his world destroyed, and they expected him to be worried about his own life! "The only thing I intend to give to you is a laser blast through the head."

The alien stiffened. "Very well." Motioning to two guards, the alien added, "Section X extractor. Take him!"

As the aliens grabbed him by the arms and forced him into a

corridor, Thane realised that the period of his biding time was over; whatever the extractor was, he wasn't likely to survive it, he had to act now.

Without warning, Thane elbowed one of the aliens hard, forcing the other against a wall at the same time. As the first alien buckled, Thane kicked him to the floor and swung the second on top of him, grabbing his holstered blaster as he fell. Two shots later, the fight was over.

Thane started to run down the corridor.

The young boy sat before the communication screen in his father's office; a neat and compact room that had survived the attack almost undamaged. He was getting worried. His mother and father had not come to help him, and it was all so quiet. Where were they? Why hadn't anyone answered?

"This is Jonathan," he repeated into the microphone below the screen.

The screen remained dark and the boy felt his lip tremble. His father had told him to use this machine if he needed him when he wasn't there, so why didn't he answer like he used to?

"This is Jonathan." As he stared in confusion at the screen, the young boy remembered – he hadn't done something he should have done! He remembered that his father had always had to remind him to press the green button! The young boy pressed the button. "This is Jonathan," he repeated.

The screen flickered into life, and white computer letters began to form words and sentences: " . . . Voice print authorisation and identification commencing . . . print number 00917 . . . key phrase: This is Jonathan . . . key phrase and voice print authorised by base Commander . . . channel open . . . proceed . . ."

Jonathan Thane smiled and began to speak.

Laser beams surrounded Derek Thane, the heat emanating from them blistering the plastic coating on the corridor walls.

Thane gasped with pain and exhaustion, looking down at the two wounds on his leg where he had already been hit. He had timed his moves all wrong, and if he didn't find somewhere to hide soon, he knew that he would be a dead man. Dead, or, with the extractor, worse than dead! Taking a deep breath, Thane barrelled around the corner and fired a volley of shots; two aliens fell. For the time being at least, he had escaped.

"This is Jonathan," said a voice from his wrist communicator.

Thane's heart missed a beat. Jonathan! His son was alive! Before a second had passed, Thane had the communicator to his mouth. "Jonathan. This is your father."

"Where are you? Is mother with you?"

Thane felt his throat constrict. "No, Jonathan. Mother isn't with me, and I'm a long way away. Where are you? In my office? Are you alright?"

"I'm ok," said Jonathan, "except my leg hurts. I scratched it. I've been playing with the machines in your office."

For the first time, Thane felt the touch of hope. If his son was in his office and playing with machines, that meant the office had survived: and in the office was a sub-terminal for the station's battle computer, an experimental device that Thane had been working on before the attack – a device code-named COMPUTERAD. It was so simple a . . . a child could use it! "Jonathan, listen to me," said Thane.

Following his father's instructions, it did not take Jonathan long to activate COMPUTERAD, and very soon the screen was alive with coloured shapes; strange, misformed objects that gradually worked their way down from the top of the screen to the bottom. Gleefully, Jonathan watched and grasped a small control lever below. Along the bottom of the screen, a square shape moved in response to the lever.

"But this is only a game," said Jonathan, pressing a button that fired beams of light at the descending objects, "how can it help you?"

"No, Jonathan," shouted Derek Thane from the communicator screen. "I let you use it as a game, but it does other things. All you have to do is press another button!"

Guided by his father's knowledge of the machine, Jonathan quickly located the button. It lay beneath a small flap marked with the letters C E. Jonathan did not know what the letters meant, but when his father told him to press it, he pressed. On the screen, changes began to occur.

"I have to go now, Jonathan," Derek Thane said gently.

Thane ran headlong towards the cells section of the alien ship, wasting no time. He knew that he had mere minutes in which to rescue Miranda and the others and escape in a shuttle. If he didn't find them soon he was doomed! As he ran, Derek Thane mentally pictured what was happening at that moment in his office, what was happening to COMPUTERAD.

Jonathan stood back from the screen, a puzzled frown on his face. The machine was working itself! As the young boy watched, the words COMPUTE AND ERADICATE flashed across the screen repeatedly. Below, the control lever moved without being touched and beams of light lanced upwards to the strange objects that gradually moved down. One by one, they were hit, one by one, they disappeared.

Jonathan Thane had no way to know that what he was watching on screen was actually happening miles above his head. He had no idea that real spaceships were exploding and disintegrating. He had no way to know that it was the first time in history that a nine year old boy had saved the planet Earth . . .

Artist's impression © Universal City Studios.

ALIEN SPACESHIP LANDS!

If you'd like to experience at first hand what it's like to be involved in an attack on earth by an alien spacecraft, you couldn't do better than pay a visit to Universal Studios in Los Angeles.

Battle of Galactica is one of the most dramatic attractions in a sightseeing tour of the studios which has become world famous, and which attracts thousands of visitors each year.

The studios organised the tour some years ago, when they realised the tremendous amount of interest which there is in movie-making in general, and special effects in particular. The tour lasts a whole day, and visitors can experience being attacked by the shark from *Jaws*, having a narrow escape when a bridge collapses, and even crossing the Red Sea, as in that unforgettable moment in *The Ten Commandments*. And that's just for starters!

The Battle of Galactica section of the tour starts when you are riding down a lonely road on the studio back lot, and all of a sudden an alien armoured vehicle blocks your path. It is manned by two robots armed with laser cannon, and they order you on board a space vehicle of immense proportions.

Preparations are being made for lift-off when in the nick of time a colonial warrior bursts in to rescue you, among a dramatic battle of noise, flame and smoke. The laser battle scene cost over a million dollars to set up, so you can get some idea of how good it is.

It's out of this world!

THE ANSWER IS...
SPACE INVADERS

Here's a quiz with a difference. Instead of having numbers, the answers spell out SPACE INVADERS – the answer to the first question begins with S, the answer to the second question with P, and so on. Test your knowledge of space and astronomy, then check your answers at the bottom of the page.

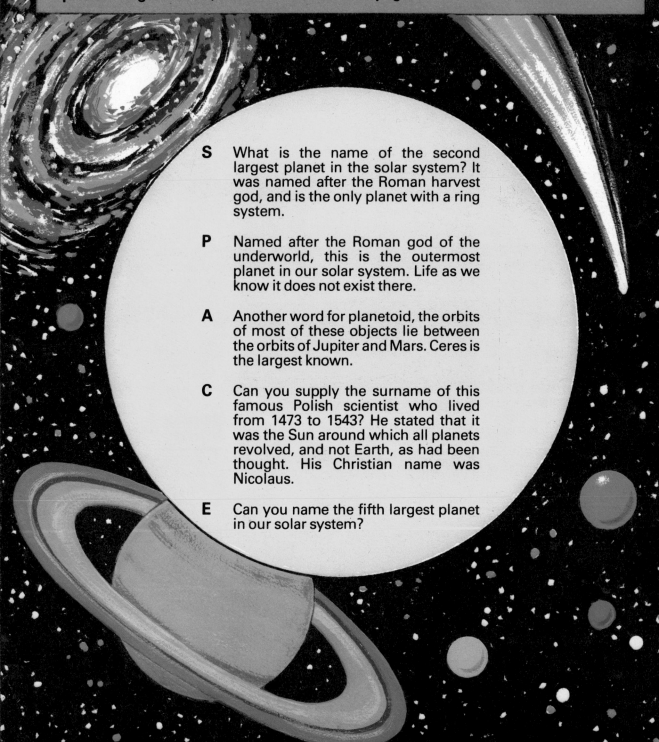

S What is the name of the second largest planet in the solar system? It was named after the Roman harvest god, and is the only planet with a ring system.

P Named after the Roman god of the underworld, this is the outermost planet in our solar system. Life as we know it does not exist there.

A Another word for planetoid, the orbits of most of these objects lie between the orbits of Jupiter and Mars. Ceres is the largest known.

C Can you supply the surname of this famous Polish scientist who lived from 1473 to 1543? He stated that it was the Sun around which all planets revolved, and not Earth, as had been thought. His Christian name was Nicolaus.

E Can you name the fifth largest planet in our solar system?

I This is the classification name for planets that are between the Earth and the Sun, ie. Mercury and Venus.

N What is the name of this planet, discovered in 1846? Its satellites are called Triton and Nereid.

V What is the name of the brightest planet seen from Earth? It is named for the Roman goddess of love and beauty.

A What is the name of the constellation in the northern celestial hemisphere that lies south of Cassiopeia and joins up with Pegasus in the west?

D Can you give the more common name for Sirius, the brightest star in the heavens?

E In astronomy, what is the name given to the partial or total apparent obscuring of one heavenly body by another?

R By what name is the planet Mars commonly known? It gets the name from the colour of its crust, thought to be caused by the presence of iron oxide.

S What is described here? The centre of the solar system, it is a glowing ball of hot gases. Its most common elements are hydrogen, helium, calcium, sodium and iron.

THE SHUTTLE STORY

For many years it was just a dream, now it's become a reality. The Shuttle is the space vehicle with a difference. It is re-usable, requiring only two weeks after a mission for checks and repairs before it can be launched again.

The Shuttle has opened up vast new possibilities for the exploration and exploitation of space. It could launch a spaceship to explore the outer solar system, or perhaps even the asteroid belt, some 200 million miles away. Less dramatically, but perhaps even more importantly, it could help to construct a base in space for solar energy projects, and it can carry all the paraphernalia for scientific experiments and technological research which cannot be carried out in the contaminated atmosphere of Earth.

Since the Shuttle programme was announced, more than 8,000 people have applied to NASA to be astronauts, but less than fifty have been chosen. Shuttle astronauts don't have to go through the rigorous selection and training procedures of the previous men in space, but they do need to have very wide experience of flying all types of aircraft, and they have to pass a fairly stringent medical. Other members of the crew may only have to pass the medical, and in some cases the only requirement is that they have good eyesight. It is hoped that in the future ordinary members of the public will be able to travel on the Shuttle, just for the exciting experience of a round trip in space. These sightseeing trips need not necessarily be that far away from reality, but it is likely that they will be expensive, especially at first.

The whole idea of travel on the Shuttle is intended to be more like travelling on a comfortable aircraft, and

quite different from the uncomfortable-looking, cramped conditions endured by the early astronauts. And one good example of this is the food.

The first men in space dined off a lacklustre selection of foods in paste form, which they had to squeeze into their mouths from tubes. Dinner wasn't really something you looked forward to when it consisted of fish paste, followed by meat paste, followed by chocolate paste for dessert.

But all that's changed now. The US Aeronautics and Space Administration has certainly paid a lot of attention to the catering arrangements on board the Shuttle, and it has prepared menus based on no less than 74 different foods, and 20 drinks.

The food will be served at tables, and it will arrive piping hot from a purpose-built oven. A typical breakfast meal might be orange juice, scrambled eggs, sausages, hot rolls and coffee, while for lunch it might be a choice of a ham or cheese dish, followed by fruit. At the evening meal, however, there would be a real four star selection of dishes. Perhaps shrimp cocktail, followed by steak, and broccoli au gratin, and even a portion of strawberries to round off a meal that would be truly out of this world.

Travelling on the Shuttle will in general be a much more comfortable ride than in the spacecraft of the early astronauts, and it will also open space travel up to much greater numbers of individuals.

It has tremendous potential but, of course, as with all new developments, there are problems to overcome, and there is also the factor of cost. If the plans to launch one Shuttle a week come off, however, that last problem should be overcome.

Oddly enough, there is a worldwide lessening of interest from the man in the street as regards space travel in general. Many people feel that we have enough problems to iron out here on earth, before expending millions of pounds in space research.

The counter argument to that, of course, is that what we discover in and about space could well be of great importance to science and technology here on earth. And the Shuttle could well be the space vehicle which finally tips the balance of the argument.

It looks like being an exciting time in space travel.

JETTISON POD

The jettison pod hurtled through the atmosphere towards the surface of the dark planet far below. Inside, Kloor, the sole inhabitant, worked desperately to keep it stable, his many tentacles racing over the control board making whatever adjustments they could. Already, he could feel the temperature rising as the pod, reaching suicidal velocity, turned first red hot and then white hot. He knew that he would not achieve a safe landing, but at least he could try to ensure that he survived the impact. He *had* to! As he plummeted closer and closer to the ground, Kloor cursed those who had attacked his ship and hoped that he was not already too late to warn the people of Earth of the danger that was to come . . .

TOP SECRET
MANAVILLE MISSILE BASE
TRESPASSERS WILL BE SHOT

The weather-beaten metal sign reflected dully in the glare of David Blane's car headlights. Spotting it, Blane slammed his foot on the brakes and looked for the entrance that the sign implied, wishing that these sort of places were not so hard to find. Then, picking the entrance out of the darkness, he reversed slightly and turned right into a small driveway which led up to a guard's hut, pulling his pass from his pocket. The guard looked at it carefully and then, satisfied, motioned Blane through. Blane thanked him and drove on and up into the main section of the base.

As Blane pulled up to the front of the base's control building, an old man in a white coat dashed out to meet him. "David," he said excitedly, "good of you to come."

Blane stepped from the car and shook hands. "From what you told me on the phone, I could hardly refuse. An alien, you say?"

"That's right," the old man answered, "a real-life, out-of-the-sky alien. Crashed right on our very doorstep! Hard to believe, isn't it?"

Blane didn't answer directly. After two years working for the army's UFO Investigation Team he was getting used to the unbelievable. But a *real alien*! It *was* hard to believe. "Has it communicated?" he asked.

The old man shook his head. "The crash injured it badly. At the moment it's in a guarded room while we wait for it to wake up. We don't know enough about its physiology to help it with our medicines. But come, let me show you."

The old man led Blane down corridor after endless corridor, until finally they came to a section marked GRADE 1 SECURITY ADMITTANCE ONLY in large red letters. The old man placed a card in a slot in the door and it *whished* open with a sigh of compressed air.

On the other side, a short passage led down to a single cell with bars across the door. Blane tried to see its occupant, but his view was blocked by a soldier who cautiously opened the cell bars and stepped inside.

"Half-hourly check," said the old man. Blane nodded.

Suddenly, the air was split by an unearthly roar. In the cell, the soldier jumped in surprise and turned to run out, but it was too late. As Blane and the old man watched, the soldier seemed to fly back and crash against the wall. There was another roar. The alien was awake! Recovering from shock, the old man slammed his hand against an alarm button and, within seconds, the corridor was full of running men, rifles held ready. There was yet another roar and the cell bars buckled, grating and groaning as the alien wrenched them from their hinges! Then the alien was out, and Blane stood almost face to face with the most horrible thing he had ever seen!

The alien stood over seven feet tall. Where, on a human, arms and legs would have been, there were hundreds of writhing tentacles, darting and twisting like a colony of mad snakes! Instead of a head and a face, the alien had only a mass of yellow eyes, and from what appeared to be a mouth, layer upon layer of slimy, dripping fangs stuck out! The alien hissed and gargled obscenely, and then, with another roar, it raced off down a corridor, leaving a trail of bubbling green slime behind it.

For a few seconds Blane, the old man and the soldiers were frozen to the spot, unable to comprehend what they had just seen. Then, with a barked command, the leader of the soldiers led his men off in pursuit. Blane and the old man followed.

They cornered the alien in a laboratory. Seemingly out of steam, it stood by a wall and made no move to escape when the soldiers moved in around it, their rifles aimed and ready to fire. Blane and the old man entered the room too late to stop them pumping four bullets into its body. With an agonised moan, the alien collapsed to the floor.

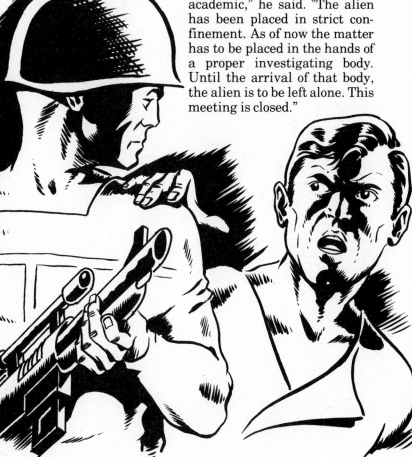

"I don't care what it looks like or what it did," shouted Blane, "you shouldn't have shot it!" His outcry was directed at the soldiers' leader and everyone else who sat around the conference table at the hastily-convened meeting. Blane was angry. Alright, he admitted to himself, the alien attacked a guard and tried to escape, but does that necessarily mean that it's hostile? It could have been confused, frightened, anything! "Do you really want," he said to the others, "to kill the first alien that comes to Earth?"

"It is dangerous," said the soldiers' leader. "Would you have preferred that we asked it to step back into its cell?"

"No!" shouted Blane, getting increasingly annoyed. "But at least you could have *tried* to communicate before shooting it down!"

At the head of the table, the old man stood up and called for silence. "These arguments are academic," he said. "The alien has been placed in strict confinement. As of now the matter has to be placed in the hands of a proper investigating body. Until the arrival of that body, the alien is to be left alone. This meeting is closed."

Later, making his way down the dimly-lit corridors towards the room he had been allocated, Blane reflected on what had been said at the meeting. He could understand the feelings of the others; the alien *was* revolting to look at, but it didn't automatically follow that it had to be evil. Too many mistakes had been made in Earth's past because men had judged by appearances only, and Blane didn't want a mistake to occur here, particularly as he was involved. He didn't . . .

Suddenly, Blane's thoughts were cut short as something clamped down over his mouth. His breath muffled, Blane twisted and turned, trying desperately to escape the grip of his unknown assailant. As he tipped his head back, he realised with horror what was staring down at him. It was the alien! It had escaped!

Trying frantically to break loose, Blane was carried off down the corridor. Although two of the alien's tentacles covered most of his face, he could see where they were going, and he knew that the alien was taking him outside. En route, they passed the new cell in which the alien had been confined, and Blane saw that the two guards were slumped unconscious — or dead — in its rear. Blane wondered what fate the alien had in store for him, but realised with horror that whatever it was, he could do nothing to help himself.

The alien carried Blane across fields and through bushes, dodging security patrols, until eventually they came to a piece of land that was split down the middle by a burnt-out channel in the ground. Blane suspected that this was the furrow that had been made by

the alien's craft as it crashed and his suspicions were confirmed when they came to the end of it. There, still smoking with heat, lay the alien's spaceship, a pyramid-shaped thing unlike anything that Blane had ever seen before. Ducking into a hatch, the alien carried him inside.

Although frightened out of his wits, Blane could not help but be astounded by what he saw inside the spaceship. Bank upon bank of flashing lights lined the walls and, here and there, strange devices hummed with power. It was only when the alien took a circular object from a slot and applied it to Blane's throat that he once again began to fear for his life. Soon after though, when the alien took another disc and applied it to his own throat, Blane realised that it was foolish to think that way. The

alien would not have brought him all this way just to kill him.

"This is a translator disc," said the alien, suddenly able to speak perfect English. "It allows me to speak to you and you to speak to me in a fashion that we both understand."

"Who are you?" said Blane.

"My name is Kloor, and I am here to help you."

"Is that why you attacked three of our guards and kidnapped me?"

The alien sighed. "I could not help myself when I awoke. My injuries had ... confused me. The other attacks were necessary for me to escape. I am glad that a guard was not mounted on my ship; I would have regretted having to cause further harm."

Blane hesitated. Kloor seemed sincere enough, but could he be sure that he was telling the truth?

Seemingly aware of what Blane was thinking, Kloor spoke. "I shall tell you how I came to be here," he said.

According to Kloor, he was a member of a race called the Antrassi. For thousands of years they had fought against the galaxy-conquering schemes of another race, the Bokassa, thwarting their plans whenever they could. Now, the Antrassi had learnt that the Bokassa planned to invade Earth itself, and Kloor had been despatched to warn the inhabitants. Before he could make contact, however, his ship had been attacked by a Bokassan force, and he had been forced to jettison, crash-landing in a field in the Manaville Missile Base grounds. Kloor had been forced into desperate action because he knew that the Bokassa would send people after him, to kill him before he could give his warning. Kloor now needed Blane to help him convince the others, otherwise, unless they prepared to defend themselves, the people of Earth would be annihilated!

Blane sagged back in his chair. It was an unbelievable story, and yet he knew he had to believe it. The things he had seen in the past day testified to that! But even now that he knew, what could he do? Kloor would now be a hunted person, an escapee not to be trusted and, more than likely, Blane would be considered an accomplice! *What could they do?*

Kloor answered the question for him. "We have to go back," he said.

Kloor and Blane moved cautiously across the fields back to the main building, concealing themselves behind bushes or lying flat on the ground whenever a security patrol passed near. Kloor had given Blane a weapon — to stun only, he had said — and Blane clutched it to his chest, knowing that it might be the only chance of success that he and Kloor had. Kloor himself carried a larger weapon, but he had stated before they left the spaceship that he would only use it against the Bokassa, if they appeared. Kloor's weapon was designed to kill.

The pair of them managed to reach the outside of the building without hindrance, and knelt below a window that looked in on the conference room. The room was empty. As Blane moved to lift the window, a voice blared out across the grounds, amplified many times over by loudspeakers.

"ALL SECURITY PERSONNEL. THE ALIEN AND DAVID BLANE ARE ON THE GROUNDS, PROBABLY ARMED AND DANGEROUS. THE ALIEN IS A KILLER. TAKE NO CHANCES. ON SIGHTING EITHER OF THEM, SHOOT TO KILL. REPEAT. SHOOT TO KILL."

Kloor nodded and turned to Blane. "The Bokassa have arrived," he said. "They have already convinced your people that I am a liar, that I am some form of criminal. It is their usual trick."

"Why should they listen to the Bokassa," Blane objected, "when they won't listen to you? They shot at you, don't forget!"

"When you see the Bokassa, you will understand."

Blane didn't know what Kloor meant by that, but he knew that it was not the time to ask questions. They had to act quickly and expose the Bokassa before it was too late! The words *shoot to kill* emblazoned on his mind, Blane opened the window and he and Kloor slipped inside.

When they were first shot at by guards, Blane was surprised that he had no hesitation in returning fire. Stunned, the guards crumpled to the ground. After that, he became used to the weapon, and whatever 'obstacles' he came across were dealt with quickly and efficiently. Blane had never been a fighting man, so his prowess with the weapon — because it was superior technology —

For a brief moment Blane thought that Kloor might have been lying after all, then one of the Bokassa pulled a weapon from under his uniform and fired.

The shot caught Blane in the shoulder and he crashed into the wall behind him. Kloor sprang into action immediately, lifting his weapon and retaliating, and the Bokassa who had fired disappeared in an electrical flash. Unsure of how to react, the old men and the soldiers darted about in confusion. Also pulling a weapon, the other Bokassa fired and rolled behind a desk. Kloor fired and the desk blew into a thousand fragments. Cornered, the Bokassa started a dash for the door. Surprised at his own agility, Blane leapt up and dived through the air after him, sending the two of them crashing to the floor. The Bokassa fought like a madman,

made him realise just how easily the Bokassa could conquer Earth if they had the chance. That realisation inspired him and after a short while, he and Kloor had successfully fought their way to the central control room. The old man, the soldiers and two other men spun round in surprise as he crashed through the door.

"Don't move!" Blane shouted.

The group in the room froze. Slowly, Blane and Kloor moved in. The old man looked at Blane as if he had gone mad.

"Where are the Bokassa?" Blane demanded.

The two men who had been with the old man and the soldiers when Blane and Kloor burst in moved forward. "We are they," they said, and suddenly Blane knew what Kloor had meant by saying that his people would be more likely to listen to them. The Bokassa were, in every way, human in appearance! By some galactic twist of fate, evil aliens from the other side of the universe had developed to look like men!

but eventually Blane restrained him and knocked him cold with a blow to the head. Gasping with relief, he picked himself up and winced. In all the chaos he had forgotten all about his wound!

The next few minutes were spent explaining to the old man and the soldiers just what had been going on. At the end of it, Kloor assured them that they were in no further danger from the Bokassa. Now that they knew Kloor had warned Earth they would not attack. They did not like battles where surprise was not on their side.

Finally, Blane turned to the old man and said, "Without Kloor's help, Earth would have been attacked. After keeping him prisoner, shooting at him and ordering him killed, I believe you owe him an apology. After all," he added with a smile, "he *is* the first alien visitor to Earth!"

The old man nodded and moved over to Kloor, not forgetting that fact. Straining his neck to look up at the seven-foot, green, multi-tentacled thing with fangs, he decided that he would never, ever again, judge things by their appearance!

DANGER! FALLING RESEARCH STATION!

In 1979, the American research station in space, Skylab, had come to the end of its useful working life, and it became obvious that it would soon fall back to earth. We had plenty of warning, and there was even time for some manufacturers to make quite a bit of money with Skylab Protection Kits, which were soon on the market in the USA.

Skylab was constantly tracked during its return to earth, and as it happened it fell on an isolated part of Australia and no one was hurt. The subject became something of a joke, but it would hardly have been so had the huge chunks of metal and machinery fallen over a populated city.

And the amazing thing is, objects falling to earth from space are by no means a rare occurence. Skylab received publicity because of its size, but hardly a day goes by without something or other coming crashing to earth somewhere.

But take heart. It isn't quite as dangerous to go out of doors as it might sound. For every one of the 4,500 man-made objects, which at

the last count were floating around in space, is being tracked, day and night, by a network of tracking stations throughout the world.

4,500? Yes, that's the mind-boggling number of bits and pieces up there. Of these some 800 are active satellites, engaged in communications and research of various kinds, from relaying TV programmes to sending back data on weather conditions.

As for the other 3,700, well, they're what you might call 'space junk'.

Some old space vehicles which have outlived their usefulness have been blown up by destruct mechanisms triggered by earth, and their components make up a large proportion of the total. Then there are metal panels, and so on, which have broken off active space vehicles, together with an assortment of nuts and bolts. One other item of note is an astronaut's glove, which is believed to be still floating around. What a find that would be if it landed in your back garden!

The catalogue of objects is subject to constant change. New bits and pieces arrive, old ones drift off into deep space, and some eventually drop back to earth.

Anything falling to earth which is liable to cause any danger is tracked by the system of tracking stations, and the results are fed into the specialised computers located at the Space Defence Centre inside Cheyenne Mountain, near Colorado Springs in the USA. One of the links in this worldwide chain is the £45 million Ballistic Missile Early Warning System station at RAF Fylingdales, near Whitby in Yorkshire. The station is primarily intended for defence, but also performs the routine task of keeping an eye on the debris which litters the space around our planet.

Huge advances have been made in space exploration. What a pity we haven't followed one of the basic rules which is so important down here on earth, and taken our litter home with us. Let's hope other civilized races of people out there, if they do exist, are a bit tidier than us!

PLANTS OF DOOM

Captain John Haydon stood before the viewing screen on the bridge of *Starstreak* and watched as the shape of Space Station Gamma gradually approached. "There it is, gentlemen," he said, turning to face the two passengers who stood behind him, "your home for the next six months."

"Thank you, Captain," said Doctor Smythe. "Xavier and I are looking forward to continuing our researches."

"Indeed," Xavier agreed with a nod. "Space Station Gamma has the best laboratory facilities in space, and the best staff. How long before we can expect to dock?"

Haydon smiled. The scientists were obviously eager to get aboard. Haydon also wanted to get them aboard as soon as possible: he had been bored by this assignment ever since they had left Earth two weeks before. Once it was over, he knew that he and his crew would receive an assignment more fitting to their talents. But, for now, the *Starstreak* was acting as a ferry, and Haydon intended to do his job as well as was possible. "Two minutes, gentlemen," he said, replying to Xavier's question. "As soon as we make contact."

Taking that as his cue, a young lieutenant flicked a switch on his console and spoke into a microphone. "Space Station Gamma, this is Earth Cruiser *Starstreak*. We are ready to dock. Over."

Haydon waited patiently for a reply. Scientists aboard space stations were notorious for their laxity in responding to communications, preferring to use what time they had to bury themselves in experiments. But after a few minutes had passed without a reply, Haydon frowned. They were not usually *this* lax. Haydon moved over and took the microphone from the lieutenant. "Space Station Gamma. This is Captain Haydon aboard *Starstreak*. Please respond."

Once again, there was no reply. Haydon turned up the volume on the receiver and the bridge was filled with the sound of static.

"Is something wrong, Captain?" asked Smythe.

Haydon shook his head. "I don't know." Turning back to the viewing screen, he took a long, hard look at the station. Everything *seemed* normal: the station rotated slowly as it should do; lights shone from portholes; signal lights flashed from the docking port. But Haydon couldn't shake the feeling that something *was* wrong. He didn't like the feel of things. "Lieutenant," he said, "there's only one way to find out what's going on. Prepare for docking manoeuvres. With or without a response, we are going aboard."

Haydon assembled a boarding party consisting of himself, science officer Macall, security officers Grant and Toth, plus Smythe and Xavier, and minutes later they gathered outside the entrance to the *Starstreak's* airlock. Taking no chances, Haydon handed them all a small weapon. After the small room had shuddered as the ship and space station came together, Haydon pressed the button that made the airlock door slide back. One by one, Haydon in the lead, the team

moved through. When they had covered the ten foot passage that was the airlock tunnel, Haydon paused. In front of him was a door similar to the one through which they had just passed. "Beyond this point," he said, "we don't know what to expect. Stay on your guard at all times. If you see anything unusual, tell me immediately. Are you all ready?" The team nodded. Cautiously, Haydon activated the second door. It swished open.

The scene beyond the door

shocked them all. The room into which they looked should have been a small reception room, but instead it was a jungle! Where floor, walls and equipment should have been, green tendrils of some immense plant had spread themselves, wrapped and twisted around everything. It was like a greenhouse gone mad!

"What," said a stunned Haydon, "is *that!*"

Doctor Smythe looked blank. Doctor Xavier peered in, fascinated. "Some form of mutant

Haydon nodded. He recognised Abronsius from data-tapes he had been shown prior to getting the assignment. Abronsius was Smythe's equal aboard Space Station Gamma, but now there was one basic difference between the two men – Abronsius was very, very dead! "What caused it?" Haydon asked.

Macall, the science officer, bent down to examine the body. On the doctor's cheek, there was a dull red scar, and the rest of his body was bruised and blackened where blood vessels had ruptured. Macall looked up at Haydon. "Severe pressure to the vital organs, sir. This man has been crushed to death!"

Crushed to death, thought Haydon, by what? He knew now that something very wrong had happened aboard the station. He could not permit further exploration until a proper investigation had been launched. "We're returning to the *Starstreak*," he said.

The team began to walk back towards the airlock. Still shocked by the death of his fellow scientist, Xavier accidentally kicked one of the plant tendrils. An almost imperceptible shiver ran through the vegetation. Xavier didn't notice as one of the tendrils suddenly began to move towards him!

"Doctor, look out!" yelled Toth.

Xavier spun round and screamed. The whole room had suddenly erupted into life. Tendrils writhed and lashed about, and those lying on the floor began to undulate like waves. The plant was alive! Xavier tried to run to the airlock, but before he could move, a tendril twisted itself around his ankle, gripping it like a vice. "Haydon, help me!" he screamed.

Haydon and the others wasted no time springing into action. Directed by their captain, the security men fired

doctor stepped out of the airlock.

"Wait!" cried Haydon. "Doctor, don't touch anything!" Haydon knew it was all well and good deciding to find the staff, but he had a funny feeling that they might *not* find them. The fact that they had not responded to the *Starstreak's* calls made him fear the worst, and until he discovered *why* they hadn't he did not want to jeopardise the lives of his crew by blundering into a situation they knew little about.

As it happened, though, Haydon's warning cry was redundant. Xavier had stopped dead in his tracks as soon as he had moved into the room. On his face there was a look of horror. Haydon slowly motioned the rest of the team in and, taking care to step over the plant tendrils, they joined Xavier and looked down at the thing at which he stared.

"Oh no," said Smythe, "it's

alien growth," he said. "Highly active by the look it."

"Is it alive?" Haydon asked.

"In the sense that any plant is alive," Xavier said, "very probably. Otherwise, how could it have grown to this size?"

"That's what concerns me, Doctor," Haydon said, a worried expression on his face. "Why have the staff allowed it to spread like this?"

Xavier shrugged. "Experimentation. Why don't we find them and ask?" With that, the

their lasers at the tendrils, while Haydon and Macall ran back to Xavier and tried to pull him free. The plant tendrils were possessed of immense strength, though, and Haydon finally grabbed a piece of equipment from nearby and began hacking away. Green liquid spurted from the vegetation, but otherwise, it seemed to do no good. Even the lasers had no effect! As Xavier writhed and screamed as more of the tendrils began twisting around him, Haydon realised that there was nothing they could do! As he and the others watched, Xavier was gradually covered by more and more vegetation until finally he had gone, crushed to death just like Abronsius!

"The airlock," yelled Haydon, "run!"

But it was already too late. Finished with Xavier, the tendrils rose and writhed in the air, blocking the way out of the room. Haydon, Macall and Smythe were trapped! Only the two security men were safely in the airlock, and Haydon called to them, desperately ordering them to close the airlock and get help before the tendrils snaked through onto the *Starstreak* as well! Knowing that it was the only thing that they could do, the two men complied and, a second later, Haydon, Macall and Smythe stood alone, isolated aboard a space station under siege from a killer plant!

"Come on," Haydon commanded, "this way!"

Before the plant could react, Haydon punched the button that opened the door into the connecting corridor, and

pushed Macall and Smythe through. As soon as he had followed them, his worst fear was realised. More tendrils lay along the corridor floor outside. By the look of things, the plants had taken over all the space station! Tendrils began to rise . . .

"It can sense we're here!" Haydon yelled. "We have to find somewhere clear!"

"This way," cried Smythe, panic stricken, "the labs!"

Haydon and Macall raced off after Smythe, trusting his knowledge of the station. The trio moved through corridor after corridor, room after room, always passing more of the plants, always having to desperately dodge and weave as grasping off-shoots snaked towards them. The bodies of station staff were everywhere;

some seemed to have died during attempts to destroy the plants, while others lay prone at the entrances to station escape pods, apparently struck down during terror-ridden attempts to break the pod seals and escape the madness. However and wherever they had died, though, it was obvious that it had been a massacre. It was only because of Smythe's knowledge of small, unblocked service corridors that the trio avoided joining them in death. The plants were everywhere! A couple of encounters en route made Haydon think that they might never reach safety.

Once, Macall tripped on a plant root and fell headlong into a mass of tendrils, but Haydon leapt in with a piece of jagged metal and hacked her free, shaking and bruised. Another time, Smythe's foot was hooked by a tendril and he found himself being dragged out of a service corridor into the main infested area. Again, Haydon slashed the tendril and, spouting green liquid, it withdrew.

Finally, miraculously, they reached their destination, and Smythe indicated a door a little way ahead. "In there!" he shouted. The trio moved in. Smythe locked and bolted the door behind him. "This," he said, "was Doctor Abronsius's laboratory. Here we might get some idea of what we're dealing with. If *he* doesn't have tapes, then no one will."

"Fine," agreed Haydon, "let's get to work."

As they started searching, all three were aware of a scratching and scraping from outside the locked door. The plants had followed them. They knew they were inside. Already, the plants had started to break their way through!

Abronsius *did* have tapes, lots of them. The problem was finding the ones that were relevant. In the end, Macall dug up one marked Project Hybrid from out of the playing machine itself. "This could be it," she said. "Abronsius could have been in the process of recording it when he died."

"Play it," said Haydon.

Macall activated the machine.

On a small tele-screen on Abronsius's desk, the face of an old man appeared. It was Abronsius. "The experimental tests we have performed on vegetation strain 331/X," Abronsius said, "have proven disastrous. I now officially record my responsibility. Because of my eagerness to perfect a self-reproducing plant I have endangered the lives of everyone aboard Space Station Gamma, and the safety of the station itself. What started as a successful growth has mutated horribly; the plants I have created seem to be able to *think* for themselves! They have, even now, killed two of my most valued assistants, and, by the time you – whoever you may be – watch this tape, I estimate many more will have died and the plants will have spread over the entire station. I never realised their potential for growth! In a few moments, I am ordering that the station be evacuated, and I only hope that we can reach the pods. By now you will know whether we succeeded. If I lie dead some-

where in the corridors, I can leave you only one thing: the knowledge that there could be a way to destroy the plants. So far, my experiments seem to point to their weakness being cold. I am sorry. I failed." With that, the tape ended.

"He was rambling, incoherent," said Smythe. "Not like him at all."

"If *you* were responsible for the death of your colleagues, Doctor," said Macall, "would you behave normally?"

"*Now*," interrupted Haydon, "is not the time to discuss Abronsius's mental state. Look!" He pointed at the doorway.

With a crack, the wood of the door splintered. A small gap appeared and a tendril poked through. With another crack, the hole widened. The door was starting to buckle!

"They're getting through!" yelled Smythe. "What do we do?"

Haydon's mind raced. Cold, Abronsius had said. *Cold.* Suddenly, he realised what he had to do. "We can get back to the *Starstreak*," he said, moving over to a carbon dioxide fire extinquisher on the wall, "with this – CO_2!"

The trio managed to fight their way into the corridor, and Haydon equipped the others with their own extinguishers. So armed, they began to make their way back to the docking port. Soon, plants were grabbing and poking at them from every direction. "Fire!" yelled Haydon, and suddenly the area was filled with a cloud of freezing carbon dioxide. Instantly, those plants which could backed off. Others, caught in the spray, writhed and were obscured in white crystals. Haydon grabbed one in his hand and squeezed hard. The tendril shattered; it had crystallised! Abronsius had been right! With a plan already forming in his mind, Haydon led the way back to the *Starstreak*.

"Captain Haydon reporting," said Haydon into the speaker on his chair as the *Starstreak* pulled away from Space Station Gamma. "It was obviously impractical to arm the whole of my crew with fire extinguishers, so I ordered ship's lasers to puncture holes at strategic points in the station's hull. In effect, I opened her up to space. The threat of Project Hybrid has ended. The plants have been exposed to their greatest weakness: the intense cold of vacuum. Report over." With a sigh of relief, Haydon thumbed the off-button. A few hours ago, he had been all ready to request a more challenging assignment than ferrying passengers to some obscure space station. Now all he wanted was a rest!

WILL EARTH EVER BE INVADED FROM SPACE?

That is a perplexing question, which no one can answer with certainty. There is no concrete evidence of any civilization anywhere in the Universe which might mean us any harm, but on the other hand it cannot be proved that such a civilization does not exist.

What we do have is a mass of data purporting to describe visits, apparently of exploration and investigation, by alien craft which cannot easily be identified. In other words: UFOs.

Let's take a look at some of the 'evidence', and some of the theories.

UFO sightings are nothing new. Through most of recorded history there have been reports of mysterious lights and sights in the skies, and many people believe that our planet was once regularly visited by alien astronauts, who passed on their superior skills to the people of Earth.

Some of the ancient stories of sightings have doubt cast upon them nowadays, because ancient peoples knew little of scientific phenomena, and could not explain mysteries such as shooting stars in the precise manner of modern man. Such a sight to them would have been evidence of the work of the gods, or a visiting craft from out of the skies.

But even if we cannot accept the ancient reports as entirely reliable, and even if we discount unreliable reports from inexperienced witnesses in more recent years, there is still a massive amount of intriguing evidence of sightings which cannot easily be explained.

There is even at least one well documented story of people actually being taken aboard an alien spacecraft. Barney and Betty Hill believe that they had this experience.

It happened on a lonely New Hampshire road in America. Suddenly a strange craft, which the couple took to be a spaceship, landed on the road in front of them, and a figure climbed out. The next thing the Hills knew they were on the same road, but some 30 miles further on, and their watches showed that it was two hours later.

What had happened during those two hours was a complete mystery to them, but when they told their strange story they were put under hypnosis, in an attempt to find the answers. The results were astonishing.

Barney and Betty were put under hypnosis separately, and both told their story. The two stories were identical, and they both drew pictures of the interior of the craft, where they said they had been subjected to tests. They both drew pictures of star maps which they had seen, and these at first puzzled astronomers who studied them. The maps showed stars which the scientists could not identify, but over the years more and more of the stars on the Hills' maps have been discovered far out in space, and always in the positions shown by the Hills.

Barney and Betty Hill were subjected to the most intense scrutiny, and the strangeness of the event caused much scepticism. Why should an alien craft travel such immense distances to an isolated spot, study two humans for just two hours, and then, apparently, travel all the way back again? It does seem unlikely, but it is impossible to state categorically that the event did not happen.

Over and over again, this is the enigma of the UFO phenomenon. The sightings in themselves often seem absurd, but if straightforward explanations cannot be found for them, we are left with no alternative but to consider the possibility that we are being visited by beings from outer space.

Is some of the available evidence being hushed up? Some people think so, and American astronaut Gordon Cooper even went so far as to say: "Intelligent beings from other planets regularly visit our world. The US government and the space agency have a great deal of evidence of such visits, but they keep quiet so as not to alarm people."

Another astronaut, Ed Mitchell, who was the sixth man on the moon, has also said: "I am completely convinced that some UFO sightings are real. The question is not whether there are UFOs, but *what* they are."

Descriptions of the various objects seen vary widely, but they are often lumped together under the general heading of 'flying saucers'. That description was first used in 1947, when an American civilian pilot, Kenneth Arnold, was flying over Mount Rainier in Washington State. It was a clear sunny day, and Arnold saw a formation of nine glistening objects, which moved towards him at incredible speed. Telling the story later, Arnold described them as being "like saucers skimming over water".
Thus that memorable phrase passed into our language.

In Britain there are two main centres of UFO activity, and the most prominent of the two is possibly the foremost centre of sightings in the world. It is Warminster, in Wiltshire.

This small town has been the scene of literally thousands of sightings, and enthusiasts constantly visit it to mount a watch on the skies. There are reports of strange lights and objects from many reliable witnesses, and it may be that for some reason this area does attract visitors from outer space. On the other hand, though, it must be pointed out that there is a school of infantry near Warminster, and it could well be that some of the incidents are connected with weapons research which is carried out there. Again, another enigma.

The other notable British centre is in Wales, and it has become known as The Broadhaven Triangle. Several reports from this area speak of tall beings dressed in silver, and lights following travelling cars. Many people have been frightened by the sights they have seen, but there are no actual reports of the aliens doing any wilful damage either to people or to property, which is a comforting thought!

And so the mystery remains. It continues, and from time to time it deepens, as another report comes in, is studied, and is never satisfactorily explained.

Many sightings are explained, of course, and among the most usual explanations are: aircraft of various types, weather balloons, atmospheric phenomena such as ball lightning, shooting stars, heavenly bodies such as the planet Venus, or simply the over-active imagination of the observer.

But some of the sightings just cannot easily be explained away. One day, perhaps, they will be. Either a simple answer will be found, or we will have to accept the fact that we are being visited by alien beings from a far distant world.

If and when that day comes, whatever the outcome is, in a way it will be a pity to know. For the mystery will be gone, and it is that very element of mystery that makes the whole subject of flying saucers so interesting and intriguing.

THE BODY STEALERS

"Activate the defence screen ... now!" ordered Jerry Paris.

Simon Lang placed the palm of his hand onto a small plate next to the doorway marked 'security room'. As he did so, the plate buzzed and the doorway, which until then had been clear, was blocked by a shimmering wall of light.

Lang then took a small disc from his pocket and tossed it at the doorway. As soon as it hit the wall of light, the disc exploded. Lang gave Jerry Paris a nod of approval. "It works," he said. "Anyone who tries to step through *that* doorway will never reach the other side."

"Now all we have to worry about," said Jerry Paris, "is getting our cargo to its destination." Paris peered through the wall of light into the room beyond. In its centre, a small black box hummed to itself.

Even now, after he had seen it working, Paris had difficulty believing that that little box was possibly the greatest weapon ever invented by man. The awareness that he was responsible for its safety until they reached the demonstration zone on Saturn sent shivers down his spine. "There are a lot of alien races," he said to Lang, "who would love to get their tentacles on that little beauty."

Lang smiled. "Stop worrying about it. Only four people on this ship have palm prints that can deactivate the defence screen: you, me, Susan Fisher and Admiral Boyd. All of us have been cleared by Earth Security. The Energy Potential Magnifier will be perfectly safe." Lang took a last look into the security room then said: "Shall we go up to the flight-deck?"

Jerry Paris nodded and the

pair started to make their way along to the elevator. They had just turned a corner when the ship's alarm began to ring. Trained professionals that they were, both men had unholstered their lasers and turned back towards the security room before the first echo had died away.

As they came back to the corner, Lang signalled Paris to stop and whispered, "Let's see just how good our security is." Paris got the idea, and the pair peered cautiously into the security room corridor.

Two aliens – of a race neither Paris nor Lang could identify – darted warily in the direction of the defence screen doorway. Behind them, one of the ship's officers lay prone on the floor. The first alien didn't hesitate when he reached the defence screen, and a second later it was dead, vapourised. The second alien stood back in shock, then regarded the doorway more cautiously. When it had seemingly assessed the security device that had killed its comrade, it placed what resem-

bled its palm on the plate. Another, quieter alarm began ringing, and the alien quickly pulled back, its 'palm' stinging with a mild electric shock that meant the plate had rejected it. The alien began to run away.

"Stop or I fire!" yelled Paris, dashing into view.

The alien spun round, starting to pull its own weapon from its belt. Paris fired. The laser bolt caught the alien in the chest and it was flung from its feet, crashing to the floor a yard or so down the corridor. It lay still.

"Good shot," said Lang, as the pair of them moved down to it.

"They're not wasting any time trying to get hold of the magnifier, are they?" commented Paris. "I wonder if there are any more of them?"

"I doubt it. These two probably stowed away during launch." Lang grinned. "At least the security system worked. Are you a bit more confident now?"

Paris smiled back and nodded. As two guards appeared from another deck, he said,

"Dispose of the body and take the other to the brig. Officer Lang and myself will be on the flight deck if you want us."

The guards saluted and Lang and Paris recommenced their walk to the elevator.

Later, as he sat facing the forward port of the flight deck and stared out at the moving stars, Paris pondered on what had happened at the security

room. Although the defence screen had worked perfectly, he couldn't shake the feeling that something was wrong. If he had had to described his doubts, he would have said it was too easy, that the aliens had acted like fools. To check a theory, Paris punched up a view of the cell in which the alien was contained. He had thought for a second that it might have been a trick and that the alien might somehow have broken free again, and even now be cracking the security system, but when he saw it lying unconscious on its bunk, his fears were allayed. Paris smiled to himself. The whole mission was making him worry too much; why couldn't he just accept that the energy potential magnifier was safe?

"Jerry Paris to deck seven. Jerry Paris to deck seven."

The voice coming from the tannoy ended Paris's thoughts, and he pressed a stud on the panel before him. "This is Paris," he said in response. "What is it?"

"Sir," said a voice that identified itself as one of the guards, "you'd better get down to the security room at once."

Paris felt his fears spring back to life. He had known something was wrong! "On my way," he said urgently and stood out of his chair. "Simon," he said to Lang, "take over."

With that, Paris headed for the elevator. As the doors swished shut in front of him, he saw his own concerned expression reflected on the faces of Lang, Admiral Boyd and the rest of the flight deck crew. All of them now knew that the journey to Saturn was *not* going to run as smoothly as expected!

When Paris bounded out of the elevator and ran along to the security room, he was stopped at the corner by the guard who had called him. "It's Susan Fisher, sir," he said. "She demands access to the security room, and she won't give a reason."

Paris hesitated. Because she had been cleared, Susan didn't actually *need* a reason, but Paris could not understand why she wanted to get in. He was determined to find out, though. "Come with me," he said to the guard, and the two of them stepped around a corner.

Susan Fisher had already placed her palm on the plate. Paris noted with annoyance that the defence screen was deactivated. When the girl spotted him coming towards her, she quickly pulled her hand away. "Paris!" she said, somewhat shocked.

Paris stopped. Even from where he stood, he could see that something was wrong with her. Susan Fisher stared blankly ahead, and when she spoke it came out hesitantly, as if she was half asleep. "What are you doing?" he asked.

Paris couldn't believe what happened next. Without saying another word, Susan Fisher pulled out her laser and fired. The shot bit into the wall just behind Paris's head! Instinctively, Paris dived to the floor and pulled out his own laser. Before he could fire, another shot whizzed by him and Paris heard the agonised cry of the guard. She had shot him! Momentarily confused, Paris hesitated before returning fire, and by the time he pulled the trigger, Susan Fisher had turned and run off down the corridor. Leaping up, Paris followed.

Susan Fisher raced along corridors and tunnels like a being possessed, and Paris had to use all his energy just to keep up with her. Once or twice, the girl turned and fired behind her, forcing Paris to leap out of the way. Finally, though, she made a mistake, and found herself cornered in a dead-end inspection tunnel. Paris sped to a halt and kept just out of her line of fire by positioning himself behind a wall. "Susan," he cried, "what's the matter with you?"

The only answer that came was another laser bolt. Paris ducked as part of the wall beside him blew away. There was another shot. Paris hissed as a piece of shrapnel tore through his trouser leg. Susan Fisher intended to kill him, too! He bit his lip, knowing that he had a choice to make. The choice was simple: kill or be killed. Wishing that he had some other alternative, Paris leapt into view and fired one shot after another down the inspection tunnel. Susan crumpled to the floor with a scream. She was dead.

Three hours later, as Paris lay in his quarters taking some time off duty, he was still wondering what could have caused Susan Fisher to act the way she did. They had held a medical enquiry in which every idea had been brought up, but none of them made sense. Susan Fisher was a highly-trained officer, and highly trained security officers did *not* go mad,

they did *not* suffer from space fever, and, most of all, they did *not* betray their colleagues. So *what had happened*? Paris grated his teeth and decided he did not like this mission one little bit. Soon afterward, the pressures of the day catching up, Paris closed his eyes and began to doze.

"Die, earthman!"

Paris snapped instantly awake. He had heard a voice! The cabin was dark. Was somebody there? Grabbing his laser from the bunk-side cabinet, Paris stood up and turned on the light. The cabin was empty. For a second he thought that he must be dreaming, but then he heard the voice again, dull, incomprehensible, somewhere at the back of his brain. Paris staggered. For some reason, he was feeling dizzy! He shook his head, but the feeling wouldn't go away. Alarmed, he strode over to the bathroom and splashed cold water on his face.

something that he wanted to discuss with the doctor. Lang left him at the door and took the elevator up to the flight deck. Paris knocked and, without waiting for a reply, entered.

Doctor Vaughn looked up from behind his desk. "Jerry," he said, "I was just going to call you."

Paris took a seat. "Any particular reason?"

Vaughn nodded. "A very good one. Susan Fisher. I think I know what happened to her."

"And me," Paris interrupted.

Vaughn leapt up. "You!" Vaughn's face darkened. "Then there's no doubt, Jerry. The alien has to be destroyed!"

Paris's eyebrows rose. "What are you talking about?"

Doctor Vaughn took a book from his desk and opened it.

Paris looked down at the open page. On it was an artist's impression of the type of alien that was currently confined in the brig. "It is known as a Skalkian," said Doctor Vaughn, "but more commonly it is referred to as a *body-stealer*."

Before he knew what had happened, he had collapsed on the floor. Everything went black.

"Paris!" said the voice of Simon Lang. "Paris!"

Jerry Paris felt something slam into his face. Where was he? Something else hit him. What was happening? A slap. Paris tasted blood on his lips. Suddenly, he was aware. Paris saw with shock that he stood before the door of the security room, his palm raised ready to press the plate! Simon Lang was holding him by the shoulders. A laser – Paris's laser – lay on the floor.

"Can you understand me?" said Simon Lang.

Paris nodded weakly and said, "What happened?"

"The same thing that happened to Susan Fisher: you tried to get into the security room, you shot a guard, you *tried* to shoot me. Luckily," Lang smiled, "I stopped you."

Paris exhaled slowly. "*What is going on?*" he said.

Lang shook his head. "I don't know."

"Neither do I," said Paris. "*That*," he moved over to a button on the wall nearby, " is why I'm placing the ship on red alert until further notice. From now on, I want anyone who behaves suspiciously, including myself, to be shot on sight!" Paris thumped the button. Red alert sirens began to wail throughout the ship.

Paris decided that there was no point in returning to his cabin, so instead he headed for the ship's sick bay. There was

A body-stealer! Paris felt his heart miss a beat. They were supposed to be extinct, killed off in some long-forgotten war! But if the thing in the brig *was* a body-stealer then . . .

Suddenly Paris found that all the jigsaw pieces fell into place. He *had* been right, right from the very beginning: the aliens had tricked them! While one alien had sacrificed itself, the other had *allowed* itself to be captured. Now, innocently confined in its cell, the alien was utilising the power which had given its species its name: the power to steal bodies by placing their minds in the bodies of helpless individuals, controlling them like puppets! It was obvious that that was what had happened to Susan Fisher and himself; they had been taken over so that their palm-prints could be used to get at the Energy Potential Magnifier! And that meant that Admiral Boyd and Simon Lang were still in danger . . .

Paris punched the intercom button on Doctor Vaughn's desk. "Flight deck," he shouted into the speaker, "present whereabouts of Simon Lang and Admiral Boyd?"

"Admiral Boyd is here, sir," came the reply, "but Officer Lang just left!"

Paris cursed. "Security, I want a squad of men at the security room on the double!" With that, Paris ran from the sick bay, taking his laser from his belt as he moved.

Paris leapt from the elevator on deck seven just as battle commenced. Laser bolts flew past guards who had positioned themselves at the corridor corner, and flakes of wall blew away as they impacted behind them. Hindered by their position, the guards could not get in a clear shot at Lang, who stood just inside the security room door returning their fire. Paris knelt and assessed the situa-

tion. Within seconds he knew that Lang would get his hands on the Energy Potential Magnifier, and when that happened there would be nothing more they could do. They would not be able to risk a shot which might puncture it because the Energy Potential Magnifier would go off like a bomb! Realising what he had to do, Paris sped off again, this time in the direction of the brig. The only way to stop Lang now was to destroy the alien itself!

As Paris thumbed the stud which opened the cell bars, the alien lay motionless on its bunk. Paris flipped it over onto its back and stared at it. It was not unconscious; it was not asleep; it was just that its mind was *not there*! Paris raised his laser ready to fire. Suddenly, the alien's eyes snapped open and it stared at him through red-tinted flesh. It had returned to its body to protect itself! Paris had no time to react when the alien lunged at him, and he

found himself crashing against the cell wall, his laser clattering to the floor. He was helpless! The alien grabbed him by the neck and hoisted him up. Paris felt himself choking. As spots danced before his eyes, Paris tried chopping at the alien's arms and kicking at its legs. The alien didn't react! Paris felt consciousness begin to slip away.

Suddenly, the sound of laser fire filled the cell and Paris felt himself drop to the floor. Gasping, he opened his eyes. The alien slid down the rear wall of the cell, a gaping wound in its chest. With one last groan, it crashed to the floor, dead. Paris turned his attention on its killer. Simon Lang stood in the doorway, a look of relief on his face.

"It forgot all about me," he said.

As Paris picked himself weakly off the floor, Lang placed a hand under his arm and helped him. Paris got the pleasant feeling that it was finally all over, and as the two men turned to walk out of the cell, a voice broke out over the ship's tannoy: "All personnel prepare' for planetfall. We are approaching Saturn. Repeat: we are approaching Saturn."

"Definitely," said Jerry Paris to Simon Lang, "the best news I've heard all day!"

TUNNELS OF TERROR

"Pro... orender... oo... receive... ove..."

Nils Borender opened his eyes and listened, sure that he had heard a voice. The cramped life module was silent and still, and through the heat haze Borender could see his assistant, Craig, shifting position on the floor, stirring uneasily in a half-sleep. Craig had not spoken. Borender frowned. They were the only two inhabitants of the module, indeed they were the only two inhabitants of the entire planetoid on which it was set, and yet someone had spoken. Who?

"Ar... oo... cop... ing... ease... respon... ove..."

For a second, Borender thought that his fevered imagination had finally begun to play tricks on him, that death was at last approaching, and then it sunk in. He had *not* imagined the voice – someone off-planet was trying to get in contact!

Borender lifted himself slowly from the floor, feeling his overalls adhere clammily to the sweat that poured from him, and shouted for Craig to wake up. They had a chance after all; their distress signal had been picked up!

Quickly, Borender made his way over to the small communi-cations desk and desperately activated the transmitter. A second later Craig joined him. Borender's voice was sluggish and exhausted as he spoke into the microphone. "This is Borender. We are receiving you. Over."

The reply from the rescue spaceship was weak and crackled with bursts of static, and Borender had to place his head next to the receiver to make any sense of it at all. He got something about unacceptable land-ing conditions and dark side and then the message ended.

His face grim, Borender turned away from the receiver. Such an abupt end to a trans-mission could mean only one thing: the rescue ship had been forced to retreat out of radio range; it had been forced to abandon them to the worst kind of sure death – acute radiation poisoning!

Borender remembered how it had all begun. Deep Space Archaeological Station Delta had been established on this planetoid to search for signs of

past civilisations, and he and Craig had been chosen to man it.

For the first six months, all had run smoothly, and they had met with immeasurable success, locating the ruins of a once-great alien city and the entrances to a vast subterranean tunnel system that criss-crossed the planet! Long abandoned and long deserted, the cities and tunnels were ripe for study, and he and Craig had been preparing to astound their fellow men with their discovery. But then it had happened. None of the mission planners had envisaged problems with the planetoid, but then none of them had taken into their calculations the behaviour of the alien sun around which it orbited. Two days ago, the sun had started to become unstable, firing tendrils of radioactive flame millions of miles out into space, enveloping

its nearest satellites. Two days ago, the sun had started to kill Craig and Borender . . .

"They can't just abandon us!" insisted Craig, banging his fist down on the piles of notes that occupied his desk.

Standing looking out through the tinted window onto the sun-scorched surface of the plane-toid, Borender shook his head. He knew that the rescue ship wouldn't just leave them, and yet he didn't know what they could do. Outside, the combined radiation and heat from the sun had already reduced what equipment they had left on the surface to nothing more than molten metal. Only the life-module's defence screens had saved it so far, but it would be suicide for the rescue ship to try to land in these conditions. What *could* they be planning thought Borender? And then the true meaning of the last message struck him. "Dark

side," he said.

Craig moved over to join him. "Dark side?"

"Of course!" hissed Borender. "Think about it! The ship cannot land here, not on the sun side! But the dark side won't turn to face the sun for another eleven hours, and the ship will be able to land. We have to get to the dark side!"

"The other side of the planet in eleven hours!" said Craig, incredulously. "That's impossible; we'll never make it!"

"But if we use the tunnels?" suggested Borender, observing the impact of his mad idea on his assistant. The tunnels! They'd not even been properly explored, let alone mapped! "Or would you prefer to stay here and die in less than four hours?"

Craig raised his hands helplessly, knowing that he really had no choice, then he moved to the desk and withdrew a rough diagram that they had made of the first few miles of the tunnels. Looking at it, they saw that it might just be possible: using the jet cycles that they had left down there, using maximum acceleration all the way, using every trick in the book it *might just be possible*. Only two questions remained, but neither man spoke them: could they be sure that the tunnels did reach as far as the dark side? And, in the darkest, unexplored regions, what secrets and dangers awaited them? Both men felt shivers run down their spines.

From the life module, the nearest tunnel entrance was roughly eighty metres away. Wearing space suits whose temperature controls were turned to the coldest possible setting, Borender and Craig began to move toward it. As they moved, the outer skin of their suits began to blister and the heat seemed to grip their throats, making it almost impossible to breathe. For one moment, Borender thought that he wasn't even going to complete the first stage of their journey, but then, thankfully, miraculously, the entrance loomed before them, and both men fell in through the doorway. The little light that penetrated from outside illuminated tunnels that sloped down into blackness. Here and there small rock protuberances and niches seemed to catch the light and warp it into grotesque shadows that crept along towards them. Craig gulped and switched on his flashlight, not killing the shadows as he would have liked, but only creating more.

Slowly, the two men moved down into a tunnel, knowing that they had over a thousand miles of travel ahead of them!

The hover cycles were where they had left them, parked at the start of a tunnel that stretched endlessly into the distance. With a nod of assurance to each other, Borender and Craig mounted the machines and activated the power. Across the dashboards lights flickered on, and the tunnel was filled with a resonant humming. Gradually, the cycles lifted from the floor and hovered in the air, their headlights marking the route ahead. Borender nodded again and the cycles accelerated.

Rock walls flashed by at high speed. The journey had begun. Both men knew that if they were to maintain this speed all along, they would have to keep a firm grip on the steering column; too many mishaps could occur doing it any other way.

as if Borender had made it anyway! Craig could see the creature clearly now, see its face with the red, slimy tongue that darted from its mouth. Craig knew that the creature would kill him if he didn't move, but whatever he did he couldn't lift his feet! Craig felt sick.

Suddenly, Borender was there, his jet cycle slamming into the creature's shoulder, sending it tumbling to the ground with an unearthly scream of pain. The impact sent the cycle off course and its side scraped along the tunnel walls, spewing sparks onto the ground. Then Borender righted it again, and was gesturing madly for Craig to remount

Once or twice, Craig nearly collided with a wall when he miscalculated a correction by a matter of a twentieth of a degree and, once, when his headlights reflected dazzlingly off a crystalline deposit in the rock, Borender almost lost a leg, missing an outcrop of rock by centimetres! Soon, though, the pair got the feel of the tunnels and proceeded quite smoothly. For the first time, Borender thought that his hopes of success may not have been misplaced. And then it happened . . .

The figure appeared before them seemingly out of nowhere, a grotesque green reptilian whose multi-faceted eyes seemed to glow in the dark. Borender gasped in shock and fear, his heart pounding, and swung his cycle to the side to avoid a fatal collision. As he flew by, the creature turned after him and hissed angrily, launching some form of spear from its hand. The spear clattered off the cycle's rear engine pod. Borender yelled and gunned the cycle faster, pulling every last iota of power from its innards. What was it? And where was Craig?

Craig had stopped his cycle. He didn't know why, except that when he had spotted the creature, he had let go of the accelerator and the cycle had dropped and skidded to a bouncing halt on the floor of the tunnel. Now, fear held him frozen while the creature advanced slowly towards him. From a distance, Craig could hear the sound of Borender's cycle and an occasional yell from his companion. It seemed his own cycle. The immediate threat removed, Craig complied, and the pair were soon back on course, hurtling away from the thing, whatever it was.

Borender had his own theory. The creature had to be a survivor of whatever race had inhabited the planetoid, that much he knew for sure. But what it was doing in the tunnels and how it had survived he had no idea. Whatever happens now, thought Borender, we must not stop – if *one* could survive, then so could others!

They had travelled a long way before they caught sight of any more of the creatures, but what they saw made them wish they could have come across them one by one every five

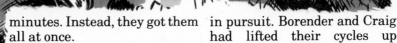

minutes. Instead, they got them all at once.

The cycles passed into a chamber formed by the junction of five separate tunnels, and Borender landed his cycle to determine which branch they should take. As he moved around with his directional compass, Craig explored the tips of each of the passages and cried out to Borender when he reached the fourth. Borender moved over to him. A shaft in the floor of the tunnel led down to a vast cavern about fifty feet below. In it, hundreds of the reptilians moved about, clawing and scraping the walls, hissing and howling, looking up at the two men.

"Run!" cried Borender, and Craig didn't argue.

Within seconds, the reptilians had poured out of the shaft in pursuit. Borender and Craig had lifted their cycles up near the roof and now hovered there, terrified, just out of the reptilians' reach. Borender screamed as the tongue of one of them managed to latch onto his ankle, but he broke free and lifted a little higher. Despite his terror, Borender could not help but feel awed by what he saw, the scientist within him reeling at the discovery of a complete civilisation still living in the tunnels, a civilisation he had assumed to be extinct aeons before!

Borender didn't get his priorities wrong, though, and when his compass indicated the correct direction, he and Craig accelerated out of the chamber, leaving the reptilians far behind.

The two cycles sped blindly

down the tunnels, propelled by men with more fear than reason in their minds. Never, ever, could they have expected this! Without slowing, Craig lifted his chronometer to check the time they had been in the tunnels. Nine hours. Two hours to go. *If* they were going the right way, he thought, because he didn't really know anymore. Mouthing a silent prayer, Craig indicated the time left to Borender, who nodded.

Taking every opportunity he could, Borender watched Craig carefully. Sweat was pouring from the man's face and his flesh was pure white. Craig is close to a crack-up, thought Borender, and he wasn't surprised. What they had seen was enough to drive any man mad. But Borender knew that he couldn't afford to have his assistant turn insane on him now; *both* their lives depended on them helping each other.

"Borender!" screamed Craig.

Borender snapped his eyes back ahead of him. More reptilians had appeared ahead! My God, his mind cried out, how many of them are there? Borender glanced up and felt panic grip him. The roof was far too low in this section to allow them to fly over the creatures; they would have to go through them!

Taking a deep breath, Borender dropped the cycle a couple of feet and accelerated to maximum, knowing that Craig would follow his move. The reptilians seemed to race toward him. Closing his eyes and holding on course, he waited for the impact, which came a second later, jerking the front of his cycle upward and splattering his helmet plate with green reptilian blood! The cycle's engine whined in protest, but Borender didn't really care if it blew up under him; all he wanted to do was get away! A second later, Craig joined him and Borender thanked the stars. "Craig? Are you alright?" he said through the suit intercom.

Craig didn't reply, and Borender turned his head to look over at his assistant. Like his own, Craig's cycle was smeared with flesh and gore, but Borender saw immediately that something more than that was wrong. Craig's cycle was weaving and bouncing erratically, more than once skimming the walls and roof of the tunnel. Craig himself seemed to be slouching over the controls and with horror Borender realised that he could hear Craig laughing! Insanity, thought Borender, Craig has gone mad! A moment later, Craig's cycle crashed to the floor, cascading dust and small stones everywhere. From the man's back, a reptilian spear stuck out rigidly. Calmly, Borender assessed that one of the last reptilians must have survived and that the spear had lodged

"I had no choice, sir," said the young officer after the crew of the rescue ship had brought Borender's body to the surface. "He attacked me as soon as I approached. I *had* to kill him."

"Understood, Lieutenant. We lost five men in those tunnels because of Borender and his assistant. I only wish I knew what had made them act that way!"

"The other men said Borender and Craig looked at them as if they were monsters, sir. But what made them enter the tunnels in the first place?"

"They obviously misunderstood our message. Instead of thinking that we intended to make our way through the tunnels towards them, they thought they had to make their way to us. Not an advisable action considering their physical condition."

"What now, sir?"

The mission commander sighed and turned back toward the rescue ship. "Mark the failure of the mission in the log, Lieutenant. Cause: acute radiation exposure due to the instability of the planetoid's sun. Effect: the total and irreversible insanity of the two men assigned to Deep Space Archaeological Station Delta, Professor Nils Borender and First Assistant Craig." As the commander walked back to his ship, he added, "May they rest in peace."

close to his young assistant's heart. Craig was dead.

When he felt that he had put enough distance between Craig's body and himself, Borender brought the cycle to a halt, falling to the ground with tears running down his face. It had been his idea to enter the tunnels, and Craig was dead because of it. Borender knew that he would never forgive himself, knew that even if he escaped the tunnels, he would never escape the nightmare of watching his friend die so horribly. Then and there, Borender knew that he could not continue . . .

Test your knowledge of science fiction by answering the questions below. Answers at the bottom of the page.

WHAT DO YOU KNOW ABOUT SF?

1.
The novel *1984* was written by an author whose real name was Eric Blair. What name did he write under?

2.
In the film *2001: a Space Odyssey*, what was the name of the super-computer?

3.
In the TV series *Star Trek* what was the name of
a) the starship, and
b) its commander, and
c) its Vulcan officer who had pointed ears?

4.
The Day of the Triffids was written in 1931, and a TV version was screened in 1981. Who wrote the book?

5.
What is the name of the dog-shaped robot who first appeared in Dr Who?

6.
Still with *Dr Who*, from which planet do the Daleks come?

7.
Still with *Dr Who*, which was the alien race living at the bottom of Loch Ness who planned to overrun Earth?

8.
Unscramble the letters below to find the name of a well-known science fiction writer. One of his books is entitled *The End of Eternity*.

A M O S A I S A V I C

9.
An Orson Welles science fiction radio production caused widespread panic in New York in 1938. Listeners who tuned into the programme after it started thought it so realistic that they believed it was an emergency news broadcast, and really believed that Earth was being invaded by Martians. What was the name of the H G Wells story on which the programme was based?

10.
In which film did Luke Skywalker make his debut?

WARWORLD

They materialised on a fog-shrouded hillside, seven of them, cold, confused and alarmed. They had been in the process of responding to a space distress signal, boarding the derelict cruiser that had been its source.

Moments before, they had been travelling through the stars. Now they were on a planet. It was night. Somewhere in the distance they could hear the sound of laser fire and explosions. The planet on which they stood sounded as if it was at war. Looking up at unfamiliar stars and constellations, the seven realised that they had no idea where they were. They had been transported into the unknown.

"What happened?"

Commander Adan shook his head and turned to face his companions, knowing that he could not give a proper answer to the question. What *had* happened? Obviously the distress call had been some sort of trap, and obviously they had been moved from one place to another in a matter of seconds, but Adan didn't know *how* or, more importantly, *why*. What could he tell his crew?

"As much in the dark as we are, eh, sir?"

Adan faced his navigator, Russell, the man who had spoken, and saw that he was smiling. He smiled back and felt the tension in all of them ease off. Adan was grateful that he had such a well-trained crew; he knew that lesser men and women would, by now, be terrified out of their wits. But not *his* crew – they were ready to take on the challenge of whatever situation they had been thrust into. Well, Adan thought, let's do just that. "Lasers on stun," he said. "Let's find out what's going on!"

When they came down off the hillside, they moved into a forest that was criss-crossed by a maze of trails and footways shooting off in all directions. Adan split his group into a spread pattern so that they could cover more ground, although he ensured that none of them would be further than twenty feet away from someone else.

in his life! Adan began to wonder whether these four unfortunates had been trapped in the same way that he and his crew had, and sincerely hoped not, because if that was the case then it meant that they were going to be dealing with a very formidable enemy indeed!

"Commander, look out!" screamed Harding suddenly.

Although he didn't know what the danger was, Adan instinctively dived for cover, pushing Russell and Sue Mitchell along with him. As he flew through the air, he caught sight of the others following his lead, and also of a small, metallic studded ball that had suddenly rolled into the clearing where they had stood a second before. A concussion grenade!

Before Adan knew what hit him, the grenade exploded and the shockwave sent him hurtling towards the bushes a lot faster than he would have liked. Adan landed with a thud that forced the air from his lungs, winding him momentarily, and then he was on his feet again,

As they moved stealthily forward, Adan moved his head from left to right, signalling to Russell, Gail Harding and Thomas on one side, and Glaze, Betjeman and Sue Mitchell on the other.

Sue Mitchell signalled back. She had found something.

Adan halted the group and they moved over. When they reached her, they saw that the young biologist was kneeling over a pile of four bodies, very dead, each of which bore fatal wounds caked with blood. "From the look of them," Sue said, "I'd estimate they've been dead for about four days."

Adan nodded, mentally storing the information. At the moment, he was somewhat taken aback by the *type* of bodies in the pile. He could recognise an Andromedan, a Plutonian, an Amarazite and a Clavian, beings from the four corners of the galaxy! He had never known such a gathering

laser gun primed, heading in pursuit of whoever threw the grenade.

The figure raced through the forest a couple of hundred feet ahead of Adan, darting and weaving through the undergrowth. From that distance, Adan could only make out the most basic features of his quarry, but he didn't like what he saw. The creature was alien – totally, unidentifiably alien – and Adan thought it the most horrible thing that he had ever encountered. Adan wanted to kill it, but he knew that if they were ever going to find out what was going on he could only disable it, disable it and interrogate. It was because of this that he waited and chose his moment of attack carefully.

The moment came soon after, when the alien darted from cover to traverse a large clearing, exposing itself to fire. Adan dropped to his knees and aimed steadily, lining up the laser sight on the alien's leg, then pulled the trigger. Clutching its wound, the alien

stumbled to the ground. Adan began to trot towards it. He had covered half the distance when the alien seemed to fold in on itself, and by the time he had covered the rest, it had completely disappeared, blinking out of existence in the wink of an eye! Adan gasped. There was no way that his laser could have caused *that*!

When Adan returned to the spot where he had left the others, his mind was reeling in shock and confusion, and it took a few seconds for what he saw to sink in.

Mitchell and Betjeman were dead; the concussion grenade had killed them instantly. Gail Harding and Russell had vanished, and Thomas and Glaze lay stunned in the bushes. Something had mounted a second attack while he had been away!

Adan snarled in anger and thudded his fist into a tree, swearing at that moment to have vengeance on whoever was responsible. Having vented his feelings, Adan channelled his mind towards the business at hand, and moved over to wake Thomas and Glaze. He knew now that the business at hand was one thing: survival.

Thomas and Glaze could tell Adan little of the second attack, only that a group of grotesque aliens had emerged suddenly from the surrounding undergrowth and had shot them down, presumably with stun weapons. From their descriptions of the aliens, Adan had no doubt that they were of the same race as the creature he had pursued. The two men didn't know what had happened to Harding and Russell, but

there was only one conclusion that could be made: they had been captured by the aliens and taken off somewhere!

Refusing to believe that they too were dead, Adan intended to find them. Arming himself and the others to the teeth with abandoned weapons from the clearing, they moved off into the forest.

The forest was a nightmare landscape of sound and vision. The sound of laser fire, distant and near, never ceased, and every now and then the forest was illuminated in a dull red glow, which was accompanied by the sound of an explosion.

The more ground they covered, the closer they seemed to be coming to a battle zone, and soon the undergrowth was alive with darting, shadowy figures. Adan took great care to

ensure that they were avoided. The area through which they now moved was filled with charred and blackened trees, and once or twice they passed patches that still burned ominously, crackling and spitting in the cold night air. Adan had never felt more alone and exposed, and even his breath, condensing in front of him, seemed to add to his feelings of horror.

Suddenly, a twig cracked, a sign that something was moving very close by, and he and the others quickly darted under cover.

Within seconds, the immediate area was filled with chaos. Four aliens – Amarazites, Adan saw – burst from the bushes, hotly pursued by a troop of other aliens firing lasers. The first Amarazite howled in pain as a shot caught it in the chest and it fell to the ground. Spurred by the death of their comrade, the other three turned to fight and let loose a volley of shots. One of their attackers was hit in the shoulder and was sent spinning out of control back into the undergrowth, out of sight. Another, hit in the neck, simply folded in on itself and disappeared. The Amarazites seemed to take that in their stride and turned to run again.

As Adan saw one of the attackers pull a concussion grenade from its belt, he knew he had to warn the Amarazites, and he leapt from the bushes, shouting. One of the attackers turned on him while the other threw the grenade, and suddenly Adan was in the thick of the battle!

The next few seconds became a blur of motion and activity. Adan kept firing his laser. The Amarazites turned to fight again, firing as well. The concussion grenade exploded, but luckily too far off target to do serious harm. Thomas and Glaze leapt out to help their commander. The attackers ploughed into battle. An Amarazite fell. An attacker dis-

appeared, Thomas was hit in the leg, and soon it was all over. Head pounding and lungs short of breath, Adan surveyed the damage. The attackers had all gone. The battle was won!

"Stranger, I wish to thank you," said one of the Amarazites in a weak whisper, and Adan turned to look and saw that they had not won. Not really.

All but one of the Amarazites were dead, and the survivor was critically injured, lying, twisted, next to a small bush. Slowly, Adan, Thomas and Glaze moved over to him. "You fought well," he gasped. "I hope you gain the right to leave Warworld."

"Warworld?" questioned Adan gently.

The Amarazite stiffened in pain. "The testing ground... some of us were lucky enough to discover why we are here... you must continue fighting... learn the secrets of this place... gain the right... gain the right to leave Wa..." The Amarazite never finished the sentence, his pain leaving him in one last sigh. Carefully, Adan closed the alien's eyelids over a pair of unseeing eyes.

Adan never fully understood the true meaning of what the Amarazite had told him, but over the next few months – doing the only thing he could, surviving – he began to learn more and more of the secrets of Warworld.

The four aliens that he and

his crew had found dead on their first night on Warworld were not the only races held captive there. Those responsible – the Assessors, Adan had learned they were known as – had kidnapped representatives from a thousand different species across the galaxy! The Assessors' purpose still remained unknown, but it became clear that they were the only common enemy, for none of the other races fought amongst themselves.

Out of all the things he learned, however, Adan's greatest shock came when he discovered that the Assessors they fought on the battlefield never died! The peculiar folding in and disappearance that he had seen so many times only meant that the bodies were being teleported back to their base, to be healed and returned to the battlefield! After that, Adan had ensured that the Assessors would be teleported back to base in as many bits as he could possibly create before they blinked out. Adan didn't like being used as a pawn in a game, and that was what Warworld was: a sick and twisted galactic game!

Adan, Thomas and Glaze eventually teamed up with a group of other aliens and they managed to create quite a crack assault force. It was during a march to such an assault that they were approached by an alien from outside the force, and the news that it brought was welcome indeed. Gail Harding and Russell had been found at last, alive, held captive in an Assessor camp. All Adan and the others had to do was rescue them!

Without hesitation, Adan began to make preparations. The first decision that he made was that only he, Thomas and Glaze would make the attempt, knowing that this was a task for the people of Earth, and the people of earth alone. They had all been waiting for this personal show of vengeance for a long time.

Dawn. Adan, Thomas and Glaze lay on a small rise overlooking a valley in the centre of which stood the Assessor camp. Somewhere above an alien bird cawed, but other than that silence hung like a shroud. All three men knew that they could well be going to their deaths.

"Are you ready?" asked Adan, priming his laser rifle. Thomas and Glaze took deep breaths and nodded in reply.

They moved down the hill in leaps and bounds, darting behind bushes whenever an

Assessor patrol came near. Once, Thomas had to leap upon an Assessor and pull it to the ground, but the struggle soon ended when the Assessor teleported out from under him.

Soon the trio reached the perimeter of the camp and they paused, taking deep breaths. They had reached the point of no return. When they had mentally prepared themselves, they leapt out into battle.

The Assessors spotted them immediately and the air was filled with laser fire. Adan and the others took advantage of the various objects and bushes dotting the camp and weaved and rolled around them, firing as they moved. Within seconds, Assessors began blinking out left, right and centre. Heading for the prisoners' tent, Thomas was cornered by a group, but repeated fire from Adan soon

scattered them away. Leaping onto a small rise, Glaze unfastened the concussion grenades from his belt and tossed them into the fray. Assessors flew through the air, blinking out before they even had a chance to land!

For the first time, Adan began to believe that the Assessors' teleport capability could actually work in *his* favour, for with injuries everywhere the camp was emptying fast!

Very soon, the trio stood in the centre of the smoke-filled battlefield and congratulated each other, knowing that victory would soon be theirs. Here and there, Assessors still darted across camp in confusion, but to all intents and purposes they had won! As Gail Harding and Russell cautiously emerged from the prison tent across the

camp, the first big smile that he had worn since arriving on Warworld crossed Adan's face.

Suddenly, everything stopped. Thinking that something was wrong with his vision and hearing, Adan shook his head. But *everything had stopped.* Next to him, Thomas and Glaze stood in mid-stride, frozen like statues. Across from him, Harding and Russell were the same. Even the surviving Assessors had solidified where they stood!

"For yourself and for your crew, you have gained the right to leave Warworld," said a voice.

Adan spun to face the owner of the voice and almost gagged. A pair of Assessors were shimmering into view, and from the moment they materialised, Adan knew that he wasn't looking at the same kind that he had fought on the battlefield. These were not soldiers that obediently teleported from battle to battle, gathering catalogues of injuries; these were the *real* thing. These were the Assessors responsible for the nightmare! Adan lifted his rifle to kill them . . .

And he was back on the Gemini, as were Glaze, Thomas, Harding and Russell, all looking bedraggled from their weeks on Warworld.

"We gained the right to leave!" shouted Glaze.

Adan nodded, unable to speak. Yes, he thought, they had gained the right to leave, but he felt no satisfaction. What of the other races who hadn't? What about those who had died? Adan decided that one day he would find the Assessors again, only next time it would be on *his* terms. Next time it wouldn't be a game.

POWER FROM SPACE

An ambitious plan to beam solar energy gathered by a satellite to a man-made island in the North Sea may have the answer to Europe's energy problems by early next century.

It may sound an incredible scheme, but the European Space Agency is taking it very seriously indeed, and has already asked a Dutch dredging and land reclamation firm to price the construction of such an island, and the economics of the whole project have been mapped out in a paper by experts at Imperial College.

Fifteen times more of the Sun's energy can be collected in space, outside the Earth's atmosphere, than can be collected on Earth, and the satellite would take the form of a space platform with solar cells, which would convert the sun's rays into electricity. This would then be beamed to the artificial island's receiving aerials, probably as microwaves, and from here it would be transferred to the national grids of the countries participating.

The great advantages of the scheme would be the large amounts of energy involved, and also the fact that the island, constructed out at sea, would eliminate the need for using precious land resources for power stations.

The disadvantages, however, would be the initial cost of the project, and also the possible problems of passing a microwave through the atmosphere, which might cause radio interference or even more serious problems.

SOLE SURVIVOR

His merciless attack on the Earth Colony Antiles completed, War Robot X-1-11 strode across the flight deck of the battle cruiser *Annihilator*, the features on his mechanical face coming as close to an expression of triumph as was possible for one of his kind. Around him, his subordinates moved purposefully in the aftermath of battle, shutting down the lethal laser cannons with which they had strafed the planet, and bowing and nodding respectfully. X-1-11 had led his race to a glorious victory, and they were acknowledging him!

"Status report," said a mechanical voice which came from loudspeakers across the flight deck. "Planetary Defence Satellites: destroyed. Surface Missile Silos: destroyed. Communication Centres: destroyed. Primary Population Zones: destroyed. Evaluation of attack: successful. Earth Colony Antiles is dead."

X-1-11 nodded and walked over to the observation window which looked down on the planet far below. Where once the lights of cities had shone brightly in the night sky, there was only darkness and the dull flickering of fires as they consumed what remained of buildings and roads. Here and there, palls of black smoke drifted aimlessly in the breeze, marking the sites where humans had died during their desperate attempts to defend the colony against the might of the Robot Empire.

X-1-11 decided that he liked that phrase; *the might of the Robot Empire*! The might of X-1-11! He was sure that when he returned to home-world, he would be honoured. Perhaps one day, he decided, he might even be allowed to lead an attack on the planet Earth

itself! Then he would be able to achieve his one desire: the final annihilation of the human race! But for now, X-1-11 knew that he would have to be content with the destruction of Antiles, be content with the fact that he knew there were no survivors. With that in mind, he turned and walked away from the window. X-1-11 did not see the light that appeared soon after, flicking on and off in the ruins of one of the missile silos: on and off, on and off. It was a sign that someone *had* survived!

John Neville kept his finger on the button of the signal light and waited. Every three seconds, the light burst into life, casting its beam across the ruins, illuminating the land for miles around. From his position atop the silo command tower, Neville watched, hoping that soon another signal light would flick on in response, telling him that there was someone else alive somewhere. He *couldn't* be the sole survivor!

But as Neville patiently waited, the only response he got

was the cries of animals and birds foraging for food in the wilderness, and he gradually began to realise just how successful the Robot Empire attack had been. John Neville was alone! With a howl of anger, he turned away from the signal light, knowing that he had to avenge his thousands of dead companions, knowing that he had to launch one final counter attack on the mechanical demons who had destroyed his world. John Neville began to make his way to what was left of the missile launching pads.

The launching pads had been badly damaged in the attacks, but one bank of missiles had escaped destruction. Picking his way past ruined equipment, Neville made his way towards them. He noted with relief that

the activating switches that would launch the missiles still survived. Without them, he could do nothing but with them, he could cause serious damage to the robot ships, catching them by surprise as they wallowed in feelings of victory. John Neville activated the silo.

"Commander!" cried Robot Z-T-16. "We are picking up three projectiles on our scanners. Their origin is Antiles!"

X-1-11 raced over to the scanner station, pushing Z-T-16 from his seat. Antiles was dead! It must be a mistake! On the screen, three blips moved closer and closer to the *Annihilator*.

"Activate defence screens!" barked X-1-11. "Prepare for avoidance manoeuvres!" It wasn't a mistake! Someone had launched missiles at the fleet! Surprised and shocked, X-1-11

watched the blips approach.

Neville's missiles missed the *Annihilator*, but impacted with the two other battleships in X-1-11's fleet. As the war robot watched, the *Destroyer* and the *Attacker* blossomed into flame, the chain reaction from the missiles' impact point rocking them with a series of explosions. Five seconds later the two ships exploded, sending shards of metal from both the robot crews and the ships themselves sailing through space!

X-1-11 stepped back in horror. He had been too full of his own glory, and as a result he had lost two thirds of his fleet. He could not hope to be honoured now! Filled with robotic fury, X-1-11 ordered the resumption of battle stations. "Prepare laser cannons! Destroy the missiles' point of origin!"

Z-T-16 hovered nearby, his mannerisms uncertain. "Commander," he said, more than a hint of fear in his voice, "that is impossible."

X-1-11 spun to face him and demanded the reason why.

"After your attack on the colony, the laser batteries are exhausted. It will be another eighteen time units before they are replenished sufficiently for a further attack."

X-1-11 felt his internal circuits begin to click furiously. Although he knew that he had made a mistake expending all the laser energy on the main attack, he would not admit it. In his over-confidence he had made a serious tactical error! If news of this was to get back to home-world he would be disgraced. With the *Annihilator* now wide open to attack, he knew he had only one alternative: he would have to take an assault team down to the planet and *personally* destroy whoever had survived! "Prepare the landing shuttle," he commanded, "and arm a squad of warriors. The humans will learn the penalty for attacking X-1-11!" As he spoke, the war robot knew

that he was not really concerned with revenge, but that his only concern was saving his own reputation.

John Neville sat back from the missile controls and smiled. He had destroyed two of the alien ships! In a small way, he had justified his own survival. Now the only thing that remained to be done was for him to notify Earth of the tragedy that had befallen Antiles. But as he leaned over to the remains of the communications unit, Neville saw the tell-tale aura of a shuttle's power drive illuminate the sky, and he knew that he had no time. The robots were coming after him!

Watching the descent of the shuttle, Neville guessed that it was going to land just on the

outskirts of the ruins, and he estimated that he had roughly half an hour before the robots reached him. In that time, he had to prepare to defend himself, and Neville knew that that was not going to be easy!

Searching out ways to fight back against the robots, Neville soon discovered that he did not have a lot at his disposal. Most of the missile silo's hand weapons had been buried in the explosions that had wrecked the buildings, and there was no way that he could dig them out in time. In the end, he managed to obtain a small flare gun and a single hand grenade and clipped them both to his belt. Some arsenal, he thought.

As he moved stealthily through the ruins, a plan began

that had fallen from its roof, bu
there was no sign of lif
"Proceed," he said.

Neville sat before an interna
monitor screen, noting car
fully the movements of th
robots as they began to file i
through the silo's main en
rance. He had switched off a
the lights in the base, and h
had to strain to see much, but h
knew that the robots would b
having even greater difficult
with their vision, so he was nc
worried. The lack of light in th
corridor would mean that th
robots would not be able to se
the first trap he had laid! As h
continued watching, Nevill
began to count off seconds: "1(
9, 8, 7 . . ."

X-1-11 stood a few feet int
the corridor, waiting while th
remainder of his men file
through the entrance. Becaus
of the size of the doorway, hi
men could only come throug
one at a time, and X-1-11 wa
getting a little impatient a
they stumbled in over loos
bricks and mortar, gropin
their way in the dark. He curse
the shoddy visual receptors tha
were built into the lower classe
of warrior robots and made
mental note that he woul
suggest future models had th
same unit inbuilt that h
himself had. *Then*, perhaps
they would be able to see a
least something in the dark
Something in the dark.

With a feeling of horror, X-1
11 realised that for the past fe
seconds he had been staring a
an obvious trap. Across the floo
in front of the doorway was
trip-wire! It could only hav
been by some stroke of roboti
luck that he himself had avoide
blundering into it! X-1-11 wa
about to call a warning whe
the last warrior moved his le
into it. Immediately, the doo
seal slid across the ope
entranceway, trapping the robo
between it and the wal
crushing its metallic skin lik
an egg-shell. A moment later

to form in his mind. Neville
knew that with such limited
weaponry he could not attack
the robots head to head, but if
he worked quickly enough, and
if he organised well enough, he
would be able to devise a system
of traps that would help him to
divide and conquer.

Hastily, Neville began to run
through all the alternatives
that he could use. Finally, he
grinned in triumph. It could
work. If he chose his points of
attack very, very carefully, it
could just work!

X-1-11 pointed to either side
of himself and watched as two
robots warriors moved off in
each direction indicated. The
pilot had landed the shuttle in a
field just outside the missile

silo, but before the robots could
enter the buildings themselves
they had to pass through the
ruins of smaller out-buildings,
and X-1-11 was not taking a
chance that some of the humans
lurked within, waiting to
attack. After they had searched
the surrounding area, the
robots signalled back that there
was no danger nearby. X-1-11
motioned them forward.

As he approached an entrance
marked Missile Command, X-1-
11 noted with pleasure that the
doorway had not been sealed
off, and he peered into the dark
corridor beyond. The corridor
stretched into the distance,
broken every few yards by the
ends of connecting corridors
and the occasional pile of rubble

the robot exploded! X-1-11 seethed; once again he had been made to look like a fool! "Follow me!" he cried to the three remaining robots. "The humans must die!"

Neville yelled a cry of success. One robot down, four to go! As he watched their leader move off down the corridor, Neville picked up on where they were heading and grinned. Their destination was obviously the reactor room, and it was there that another trap awaited them. This time, though, Neville had to be present himself; he had to tempt them into it!

The reactor room was deep in the silo's structure, a circular chamber that contained the power units for all of the base. Because of the radiation hazards associated with such forms of power, the reactor itself stood on a circular platform in the centre of the chamber surroun-ded by a deep pit. There was only one bridge across the pit and that had been withdrawn to the centre. On what was now basically an island, John Neville waited.

The robots arrived soon after, making their way slowly down the dark tunnel that served as the entrance to the reactor chamber. Neville listened as the lead robot barked commands, and waited for the right moment. When the foursome had come within ten feet of the edge of the pit, Neville called to them. Immediately, the robots scattered to both sides of the tunnel, protecting themselves behind piles of rubble, and firing their lasers. Beams shot by Neville, but he kept his body low and continued shouting. He estimated that it would take a few seconds for the robots to decide to launch a proper attack, but pulled the flare gun from his belt in readiness. Then the robots began to run the last ten feet and Neville fired the flare. Instantly, the reactor chamber exploded with light and Neville covered his eyes. On the other side of the pit, the robots blundered headlong towards the edge. His plan had worked. By suddenly changing the darkness of the chamber into brilliant light, Neville had completely thrown the robots' visual receptors! Unable to stop themselves in time, the first two robots tumbled headlong into the pit, exploding into tiny fragments when they hit the bottom. Three down, two to go! While the remaining robots still recovered from the dramatic change of light, Neville once again extended the bridge and ran. If the final part of his plan was to work, he had to get back to the control room before the robots could stop him!

X-1-11 had never really understood what the human

emotion called fury was, but now he knew only too well. While his visual receptors danced with light, he supported himself helplessly against a wall. Vaguely, he could detect the running figure of a human getting away, but he could do nothing to stop him. All X-1-11 could do was wait. Wait and imagine all the horrible things he would inflict on those humans responsible for his plight. Had he known that the destruction of two of his ships and the death of three of his assault team was due to the efforts of one man, X-1-11 would probably have exploded!

Up in the control room, Neville carefully adjusted dials on the missile launching console. Because it had veered off in a defensive manoeuvre when he had fired the first three missiles, Neville had missed the third alien battleship, and now he was resetting the fourth missile's guidance controls. After a few seconds of intricate work, Neville sat back. The missile was now trained on the last ship. With a decisive thump of his fist onto the button, he primed the missile. A green light on the console signalled it was ready for launch. Neville, though, did nothing more; he

had no intention of launching *just* yet. He had something else in mind . . .

Unclipping the hand-grenade from his belt, Neville walked out into the corridor and carefully brushed aside some pieces of rubble on the floor. Once he had formed a little hole, he nestled the grenade inside it, and then, still gripping the grenade, pulled its safety pin. Neville felt the spring release of the grenade open slightly in his hand and squeezed tighter. He was not yet ready to let go, because when he did there would be five seconds before the grenade exploded, and when it did he wanted the robots to be right on top of it!

Fully recovered, X-1-11 and the last surviving warrior moved into the control room corridor. As soon as he spotted the figure at its other end, X-1-11 stopped, a feeling of final victory building inside him. The figure, a man, was alone, and he appeared to be injured. The man lay on top of a small pile of rubble, his arm apparently buried beneath it, his face a mask of contorted agony. The fool, thought X-1-11, he has been caught in one of his own traps! Slowly, his rifle aimed at the man's head, X-1-11 moved down, closely followed by the warrior. X-1-11 knew that he could kill the man now, of course, but he wanted to question him. "Human," he called, "where are the other survivors?"

The man lifted his head. "There are none," he said weakly. "I am alone. Help me."

"None?" boomed X-1-11. "That is impossible! You expect me to believe that you are responsible for the destruction of my men and ships?"

The man didn't respond, but instead sagged back to the ground. His curiosity aroused, X-1-11 moved closer. Suddenly, the man leapt up! Realising that he had been tricked yet again, X-1-11 dashed after him.

Neville pumped all the power he could into his legs. He had to reach the control room before the grenade exploded! As he leapt through the doorway, his mental countdown reached zero and the grenade went off. Caught by surprise as they passed by it, X-1-11 and the warrior were first blown into the ceiling and then buried beneath it as it came down on top of them! For a second, dust hung in the air and the only sound was that of Neville's heavy breathing. Then, Neville moved slowly over to the missile console and pressed the green button. The room and corridor echoed with the sound of the missile launching.

A minute later, the sky above Antiles brightened as, somewhere above, the battle cruiser *Annihilator* exploded. Neville only hoped that whatever remained of the robots buried in the corridor could still hear. After he had witnessed the death of his colony, he *wanted* them to.

ESCAPE FROM ZARNON-12

RADIATION BELT

COMPUTER CONTROLS IN ERR BACK 4

MISS A TURN TO RIDE OUT METEORITE STORM

START

You have landed on the planet Zarnon-12 in answer to a faint distress signal, and have been able to give medical assistance to the inhabitants of this strange world. Now, however, when you come to take off again, you find the reason why the signal was so faint. It turns out that Zarnon-12 has a bizarre gravitational pull, which consists of random loops and swirls above the surface of the planet. Very few spaceships have ever successfully escaped.

Use all your skills as a space traveller to negotiate your safe exit from the atmosphere of Zarnon-12, obeying all the instructions as you move across the board. If you land on a *crossing square* your photonic energy drive will be dissipated, and you will have to go back to the start to build up fresh energy levels. Only if you land on a square immediately *before* a gravitational loop can you escape it, by moving in the direction of the arrow, but if you are unlucky enough to throw a one with your next throw you will still have to go back to the beginning.

One other thing! Zarnon-12 has a lethal radiation belt, which can only be broken through by vessels moving at speed. Therefore if you land on a square affected by the radiation belt you will have to throw a six before you can move off it again.